67 Years of Stewardship: The Warren Farm

A Unique Farming Story

By: Randy Warren

1

I loved the view from every window. One of my favorite memories occurred one extremely cold winter evening. It was dusk and beginning to snow. We had just finished dinner and dad was at the kitchen sink which overlooked the back yard raspberries and Christmas tree patches. He called Earl and me over to look out the window. It was a small herd of deer. They were coming into the yard up against the first row of raspberries all in a long line. The wind was blowing hard from the northwest and the deer were leaning into it as they warily pushed thru the deep snow. Earl, only two at the time, seemed entranced by the scene. We all were. It was a special few moments, almost intimate in our watching. The three of us leaning close to the cold panes of glass, awed by natures' strength and harshness.

--Heather Warren

Aerial View: photo by Earl Warren

There's a real picture-book farm with strawberries, raspberries, pears, and grapes just off the stretch of U.S. Route 4 between Northwood and Durham, right next to the University of New hampshire recreational site at Mendum's Pond,...For my last meal on earth I would choose a bowl of raspberries, and I would choose to eat them in the meadow at that farm--fresh-picked and warm from the sun.

--Joyce Maynard, "Simple Country

Pleasures," New York Times, June 13, 1982

I wish to thank my wife Heather, my friend Scott Young, and my sister Ann for their immense help with this book. My friends Charley Cawley and C.J. Bronstrup were also indispensable. Andre Cantelmo, (co-owner of Heron Pond Farm), Bill Towle (co manager of Emery Farm), and Charlie Moreno (Consulting Forester) have been instrumental by their friendship and professional involvement in the Warren Farm. My many friends and family who gave me emotional support and encouragement are too many to list.

Chapter 1: Land Conservation Easement

My father, Richard Warren had been raised on a family farm on Warren Road in Ithaca New York. He had seen his family farm split up and parcels sold over the years. By 1987, many houses, a golf course, married student housing for Cornell University, and the Cornell's Large Animal Veterinary Farm all occupied what once had been his family farm. Very little open land remained of the Warren's farm. Dad's father, George Frederick Warren, had been a professor of Agricultural Economics at Cornell, as well as an advisor to Franklin Delano Roosevelt both at the state and federal levels. G.F. Warren had written the subsidy programs for the New Deal, had been instrumental in advising F.D.R. to end

private ownership of gold, and was the most sought after agricultural economics speaker in the country in the 20's and 30's. He was possibly the most sought after speaker period. He died in 1938 and I never met the man. Warren Hall on Cornell campus was named after G.F. Warren in 1932. In November 1933, he was featured on the cover of Time Magazine. Although his farm was not his primary occupation, Grampa Warren passed his love for farming to his children.

In 1987 the state of New Hampshire voted to fund the Land Conservation Investment Program. This was the forerunner to the current Land and Community Heritage Investment Program. My father saw the press release for this program in the local newspaper. He didn't want to have his farm split up, so he was very interested in this program. Once a property is conserved by the LCIP, the land cannot be sub-divided or developed. Mining rights and development rights would be extinguished. The owner could be compensated up to $500,000 towards the decrease in land value the conservation easement produces. Any value above $500,000 would be donated by the landowner. This $500,000 was to be half paid by the New Hampshire LCIP fund and half by the town or municipality. Dad asked for an application and after talking to Mom, my siblings, and myself, explaining that this was our inheritance we were giving up, he applied. He realized that the Town of Barrington would not contribute but he was willing to conserve the land if he could get the state portion. An appraisal and survey of the farm was done. The preliminary appraisal seemed low but he would still get the $250,000 so he proceeded. The final appraisal came in at half the original value. Dad was puzzled and disappointed. He was quite upset when he heard that the appraiser had been told to make the LCIP funds stretch, and that was probably why the appraiser reduced the value. The appraiser had been recommended by the LCIP administrators. My father was determined to stop pursuing the easement, as he would not deal with "Those Crooks". The Town of Barrington Conservation Committee, whom had been involved in the process, hoped the land would be conserved and members went to the Barrington Selectmen for a Conservation fund to do a second appraisal. A conservation fund of $10,000 was approved. The Conservation Committee contacted Dad and asked if they could do a second independent appraisal that they would pay for. He agreed although he said it would be a waste of time and money, as he probably wouldn't change his mind. The second appraisal was a much more realistic value, showing how underhanded the former appraiser had been. Dad decided to go ahead with the easement. The easement was completed in September 1989. One more wrinkle was that Dad was promised that there would be no capital gains tax on the state portion. This was never pursued so he had to pay over $70,000 to the IRS when he received the

$250,000.00. By this time, both of my parents were fully vested in the goodness of this easement and proceeded despite being deceived. Throughout this process, my Mom was not happy with the easement as she thought she was giving up control of the land. She only agreed to it because Dad wanted it. Right before the

Richard and
Dorothy Warren
1989

conservation easement was completed, Mom started to understand the true details and became totally convinced that this was a wonderful thing. When the conservation easement was announced and in the local and state newspapers, a number of people wrote letters thanking my parents including one anonymous letter that was a tear-jerker. Mom died in December of 1989 from rapidly growing cancer diagnosed in late October. Her last days were spent reading and re-reading those letters. Her happiness over the goodness of this easement helped her greatly in her last days. As I had returned to the farm in 1989 for the summer, the money from the easement enabled my father to ask me to work at the farm year round. I agreed. At my father's funeral in January 1997, one of my father's best friends and the man who replaced him when he retired from the Poultry Extension Service, came up to me and asked if I knew why Dad had conserved the farm. We talked about the farm in Ithaca but he added "He told me it was the only way Randy (me) could continue the farm". And this was said before I had come back to the farm in 1989. I had not known that this was part of his thinking. When Dad died, his will still read that his possessions would be split between the four children. My siblings gifted their shares of the Fahm to me. This was done graciously because dad had hoped they would and because it was not a large amount of money due to the easement. Also they had hoped the Fahm could continue. Both of my brothers died before the Fahm left the family. A small portion of the Fahm was gifted to my sister and brother-in-law in 1989. This land abutted their house and house lot next to the Fahm. In the early 1980's they had purchased a lot that abutted the Fahm and built a house. In 1988 as Dad was arranging the survey for the easement he came to me and told me he wanted to give them enough acres to allow them to get into the NH Current Use tax program for their land. A few weeks later he told me that he was going to give them 10 acres. Shortly after that he took a hike along his western border where a mobile home park abuts the Fahm. He encountered numerous places people were using his side of the stone wall border including a small garden, a camper, and lots of trash. He got back to the farmhouse still mad and said, " I do not want to border the mobile home park anymore," He grabbed a copy of the map and put a long narrow piece of tape over that border area and that is what he gave to the surveyor to survey out for my sister and brother-in-law. It became a 27 acre parcel. This left the Fahm with 244 acres. My sister and brother-in-law still reside on their land next to the Fahm. All the gifting was made possible due to the easement. Many people have walked, hunted, birded, and relaxed on the Fahm due to the easement. In the time since 1989, many acres adjoining the Fahm have been conserved and as of 2013 this was the largest greenway in Barrington. The conservation easement allowed my wife and myself to put the Fahm up for sale in 2011 with a clear conscience. Numerous groups have sponsored conservation easement programs and talks. Being one of the first state sponsored easements, I have had the pleasure of being asked to give talks about our experience with the conservation easement. These talks were the genesis of this book.

Chapter 2: Why I Write

The story of the Warren Farm in Barrington NH, from 1946 to 2013, has many unique facets. I marvel how my father Richard Warren grew up on the Warren's farm on Warren Road in Ithaca, NY and died owning the Warren Farm on Warren Road in Barrington, NH. This land also was a unique place to grow up for myself and my siblings. The land and our parents combined to allow us a freedom enjoyed by very few at the time and very, very few today. This property also became a rare place for many other people as we invited the public for 56 years onto our farm. Pick your own and cut your own crops and our own farm stand drew thousands of people to our farm during this time. Hunters, hikers, birders, loggers, UNH students, and neighbors were also allowed to enjoy our property. This blend of place and people left me with a wonderful past to share.

I grew up in a time when many farms existed and most people either lived on a farm or had a relative that owned a farm. There was no novelty to living on a farm. Farming reflected a poorer lifestyle and I felt slighted when called a farmer. The financial realities of farming and development pressure were causing a rapid decrease in farms. As development removed most of the farms, they became novelties. It became a status symbol to own a farm. Not long after selling the Fahm, a doctor treating my wife called her a celebrity due to her ownership of the Warren Farm. I am attempting to save this knowledge so future generations can add to this. My Dad had a love for this land and I inherited that love. For the last 24 years of our family's ownership of the land, I worked and/or lived on the Fahm. Age caught up with us and we could not out-work the financial realities of farming. Our love for the Fahm meant we must turn it over to new stewards. A lot of stories and learning experiences are no longer being discussed on a regular basis now that we have moved from the Fahm. Hopefully you will enjoy these stories. Mom always wanted to name the Fahm "Peacefield". Dad wanted to name the Fahm "Poison Ivy Acres". The official name became "Warren Farm". I am calling it "Fahm" to honor my oldest brother Peter Whitson Warren who produced a written history and photographic show about the Fahm. He loved to make fun of the lack of use of the letter R by New Hampshire natives. "The Fahm" was his nickname for the property

The line that best describes the Fahm comes from my wife, Heather. Heather would say she loved "the View from Every Window". I did not realize until she started using this line that sitting in the farmhouse looking out on the view always gave me a warm comfortable feeling. I took this view for granted in my early years as possessions, relationships and wants clouded the bigger picture. Throughout my first 38 years, personal issues, geographic cures, relationships, and numerous failures provided an avenue that brought me to a different appreciation of those views. I would like to pass along what that view meant for me. To do so means showing the ingredients of parents, wife, land, buildings, siblings, in-laws, children, nieces, customers, friends, employees, equipment, weather, and nature that constantly changed those views. One of my best learning experiences was finding that although each person who came to the Fahm saw what I had done, I always saw what I had not done!

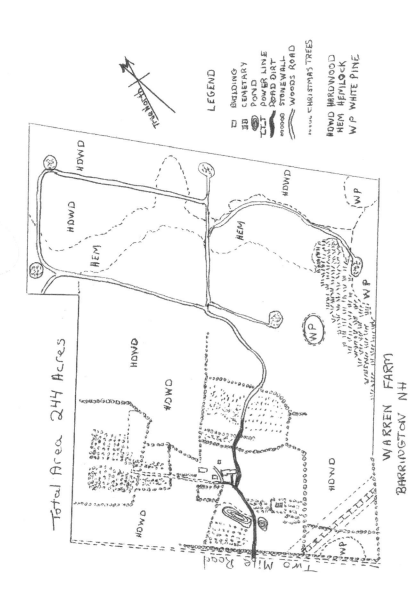

Total Area 244 Acres

LEGEND

□ BUILDING
⌗ CEMETARY
POND
˙ᴸᵀ POWER LINE
ROAD DIRT
STONEWALL
WOODS ROAD
CHRISTMAS TREES

HDWD HARDWOOD
HEM HEMLOCK
W P WHITE PINE

True North

WARREN FARM
BARRINGTON NH

Two Mile Road

HDWD
HEM
WP

13

Chapter 3: History of the Land

In the southeast corner of New Hampshire, in a town called Barrington, there is a plot of land consisting of 244 acres of slightly hilly, rocky, fertile, mostly forested land. The forest would have had a mix of pine, maple, oak, birch, hemlock, ash, spruce, beech, chestnut, and elm trees. Today the chestnut and elm are mostly gone although small trees still grow from stumps until the respective diseases kill them again. This land was probably productive even in the centuries where no one actually lived on the land. Blueberries, nuts and deer would have been harvested on this land.

A Scotch-Irish family named McDaniel (although various spellings were used finally arriving at McDaniel) held an English land grant for a large tract of land that included this 244 acres. In 1719 it appears that one of the McDaniel's and a member of the Ellis family occupied a cabin on the southeast corner of the land. The cabin had been built around 1712 to house the Ellis Iron Works crew. The iron works crew had mined bog iron from a large marsh, swamp area that was on the southeast corner of the land and adjacent properties. The iron they had mined was a very brittle inferior grade but the mining operation appears to be one of the few financially successful operations in NH. A tailings hill is still evident from the mining. Smelting evidence has been found on an adjacent property. The mining seems to have ceased when the crew moved to the area with a higher grade of ore that came to be called Gilmanton Iron Works. The company went bankrupt soon after this move. The abandoned cabin was used as temporary housing but was enlarged. By the 1740's it was called the McDaniel Garrison. During this period it was used to protect against Indian raids with 7 families staying in the garrison for 3 years. By this time, most of the forest had been cleared and there is evidence that all 7 families could see their houses from the garrison. It is surmised that the families tended their farms during the day but stayed at the garrison at night. The garrison was built on a knoll with a cellar that could house their animals for safety and warmth. The garrison was abandoned after the Indian wars ended in the late 1740's (what we call the French and Indian Wars came later). In 1760, a man named Peletiah Daniels bought 271 acres from the McDaniels that included the garrison. The garrison began to be called the Daniels-McDaniels Garrison. Peletiah and his family lived in the garrison while he built a heavy timber and white clapboard Colonial style farmhouse. The garrison was torn down in 1875.

Although modified a few times over the years, this farmhouse still stands as the main house. A small addition was built sometime before 1875 that became the kitchen. An addition in 1875 added a carriage and wood shed that today houses the farm stand. This building has the roof timbers from the garrison. The timbers were transported intact from the garrison to their current site. A diary excerpt has a lady sitting in the living room saying "How forlorn the garrison looks without its roof as its roof is being pulled down the road by oxen". A small building that we suspect was the blacksmith/cobbler shop may have been moved from the garrison property or the McDaniel property (the McDaniel farm house was moved in 1892 from the Two-Mile Rd to the new Route 4). A medium shed and a large barn are on the property. A renovation in the 1890's added a bay window amongst other "Victorian" touches to the farmhouse.

When no written history is available, history becomes subjective. Nowhere is this more evident than in the location of the garrison. A local historian came to my father in the 1960's to ask if he knew where the garrison had been. My father said he did not know, but that he had found a pile of rocks and bricks in a front field. The historian said "That is where it was!" He then put that as the location in the History of Barrington he wrote. When my oldest brother did a written history of the farm, he surmised that the garrison had been on the Two-Mile Rd straight in front of the farm house, where another rock pile had been found. In 1995, a neighbor found a picture of the garrison from 1875. When comparing this picture to the topography, only one location is possible about 1500 feet from my brother's surmised location. A few years later, another neighbor found a written description of the location confirming the location derived from the picture.

From 1760 to 1920, the Daniels family were stewards of the land. During the late 1800's a Daniels lady married a McDaniel man and both names became entwined. My father always told us, "They didn't travel far in those days". The cemetery on the property was used by both the Daniels and McDaniel families. Peletiah continued the process of clearing most of the land and making pasture for sheep. More stone walls were built on the front part of the farm, although some of the best were in the garrison location, so probably were already built by 1760. Sheep was a major commodity for both wool and meat. This continued for the next 100 yrs. In approximately 1870, we know that the town doctor resided on the farm. Many trails we found on the land probably were set up or improved during this time to aid the doctor in getting to the residents homes quickly. One particular trail we found in 1991 with cedar logs laid in wet areas, is probably the trail Clarence Calef told me about in the 1960's. As a boy around the 1910's his summer job was to drive a crew to the back area of the Fahm to pick blueberries, He would bring them there in the morning and bring them back to his family's store in the evening. Calef's Country Store is still a town landmark. After the civil war, a mass exodus occurred in New Hampshire due to a number of factors. The largest factor was soldiers from New Hampshire in Grant's western campaign had seen level, fertile, and rock-free soil along the Mississippi River. If they returned to NH it was to get their families. Wool was also declining as "Cotton became King", after the civil war, as the South's cotton was shipped to the North instead of England. Large factories replaced small factories and Barrington's small water powered mills were no longer efficient. This all led to a 2/3 decline in the population of Barrington. It was 1960 before Barrington again began to grow. In 1790, almost 90% of Barrington had been cleared of forest. In 1890, almost 70% of Barrington was wooded or converting back to woodland as fields were abandoned. By 1960 almost 90% of Barrington was wooded.

The Fahm remained in the Daniels family until the 1920's. Elizabeth Daniels Berry whose husband had been a logger, living off the timber on the land until his death in 1897, sold the farm to another logger named Carroll Foss in the early 1920's. Carroll Foss subsisted off the woodland and died at the farm. He over harvested the woodland and the timber was depleted. In the early 1940's the Harrison family bought the farm as a summer residence. Mrs. Harrison did not like the Fahm and she refused to stay overnight there. After Mr Harrison's death a year after purchasing the farm, it was abandoned. Mrs. Harrison allowed a family who hunted on the land to keep an eye on it. One member of this family continued to hunt on the land throughout our tenure. In early 1946, Mrs. Harrison put the farm up for sale.

The Fahm's southern border fronts on the Two Mile Road which was part of the road called the New Hampshire Turnpike. It is believed that one of the six toll gates was at the sight where the Two Mile Rd crosses Warren Road. It is unknown whether the McDaniel or Daniel family ran this toll gate. The Two Mile Road had been updated using private capital so it was considered a private not public road. From April of 1801 until early 1825, tolls were collected. It became a free road in 1825. The site of the toll gate is close to the original sight of the McDaniel homestead. The McDaniel house was moved to its current location on Route 4 in 1892 when Route 4 opened. Here is a list of toll prices found in a ledger at the Fahm.

Every ten sheep or hogs.   1 cent

Every horse and rider or led horse. 1 cent

Every ten cattle.   2 cents

Every sulky, chair or chaise, with horse and two wheels.
1 ½ cents

Every chariot, coach, stage, wagon, phaeton or chaise with two horses and four wheels.   3 cents

Either carriage last mentioned with four horses. 3 cents

Every other carriage of pleasure with like sum according
to the number of wheels and horses drawing the same.   3 cents

Each cart or other carriage of burden drawn by one beast.
1 cent

Each wagon, cart or other carriage drawn by two beasts. 1 ½ cents

If by more than two, one cent for each additional yoke, oxen or horse.

Each sleigh drawn by one horse. 1 ½ cents

By two horses. 2 cents

By more than two horses, one cent each horse.

Each sled drawn by one horse. 1 cent

Each sled drawn by two horses or yoke of oxen. 1 ½ cents

Of more than two horses or yoke of oxen, one cent for each additional pair of horses or yoke of oxen.

Chapter 4: The Warrens Arrive

In early 1946, Richard Warren, Dorothy Warren, and their two sons Peter and Bradley were residing in a rented house on Baghdad Rd in Durham NH. Richard who went by Dick, had an office at the University of New Hampshire and was the Poultry Extension Specialist for the state of New Hampshire. The Warrens had purchased a vacant lot on Baghdad Rd and were saving money to build their own house. The owners of the rented house were returning early and wanted their house back. There was not enough time to build, so they sold the lot and went outside of Durham to find a house they could afford. Two properties were found that interested them. Their first choice was a property in Nottingham, NH that consisted of a colonial house and sturdy barn on Route 4 with 100 acres. The Warrens agreed to put an offer on this property but found that an offer had been accepted that very morning. The property was no longer available. The Warrens then decided to make an offer for their second choice. Their offer was accepted and they purchased 271 acres with a Colonial/Georgian style house, a barn with a caved in roof and two smaller outbuildings. Years later the family, who bought the first property, sold it to a company that wanted to bottle water. The ensuing political problems ended with both the farmhouse and barn destroyed by fire and the water company bankrupt, without ever bottling any water. The house fire was caused by an electrical fire during renovation. The barn fire was ruled arson. The local protests, legal fights, and delays doomed the company.

The Fahm circa 1946, photograph by Richard Warren

Dorothy Warren always said, when describing their first visit to the farm that," the brush hit both sides of the car until almost to the house. I looked at Dick's face and I knew I was going to live there." The house had no central heating system and no heating ability other than six fireplaces. Five of the fireplaces were on the main chimney which was clay lined rather than mortar. The roof leaked, the house had no electricity, running water, indoor plumbing, or telephone. The neighbors thought they were quite deranged to have paid $5500.00 for the property in that condition and that far from Route 4. It also meant a 7 ½ mile commute, which was considered long in those days. The dirt road to the farm was maintained by the town which meant it was not plowed for at least three days after a snowstorm and its condition was so poor, that it was impassable for up to three weeks during mud season. The property was off of Route 4 in Barrington and the house was 1/3 of a mile from Route 4. The property fronted on the Two-Mile Rd, and when Route 4 was built in 1892, a town road was built to access the property, to keep the property from being landlocked. This road had no name. In 1972, Dad came home, and to his surprise, the town had erected a sign naming the road Warren Rd. All unnamed roads in town were named in 1972, during the 250th anniversary of Barrington.

In 1948, my sister Ann was born and I followed in 1951. Thus the six of us became the Warren Family of Barrington NH. Later my wife Heather became an integral part of the farm. My children, Russell, Jennifer, Richard and Earl, nieces Kirstin and Amy, and brother-in–law Denny all have had major roles at the Fahm.

Chapter 5: Dad

Dick (Dad) went right to work on the old farmhouse and outbuildings. He patched the floors in the house where the porcupines had chewed holes. His brother-in-law, John Swan helped him during the fall of 1946 to put a roof back on the barn where it had caved in. Dad had little money for the roof, so they removed the floor boards of the barn and put them on the roof. This later became problematic. For rafters, Dad cut maple trees from an area behind the house, choosing those as large as he could handle by hand. With a block and tackle he hoisted the rafters into place. As of this writing, those rafters are still in place, although plans have been made by the new owners to completely renovate the barn. Dad cut the brush that had overtaken the remaining fields with a scythe, and in the spring of 1947 planted the first Christmas trees in the back field. Ten years later, the first cut your own Christmas trees were sold from that field at $1.00 per tree. Many people thought that this was an extravagant price. My older brothers Peter and Bradley began a vegetable garden and small raspberry and strawberry patches in the mid-fifties. All summer produce was sold at a self-service stand at the Route 4 end of Warren Road. All nature of vehicles were used to transport the produce to the stand over the next 15 to 16 years, none of which were road worthy. Some had fenders, some not. Some had brakes, some not so much. Some ran well, some needed a lot of tinkering. One day in 1966, while rapidly approaching Rt 4, I went to use the emergency brake (the only brake available) on the current jalopy, a 1947 1 ½ ton Dodge dump truck. The brakes failed to slow the truck. I cruised onto Route 4 grateful nobody currently was on the road. I finally got the truck stopped, put it in reverse and it backed barely off the road before it would move no more. I was relieved that no police had seen me. I was 15.

In 1960, I came home from a 4-H meeting and much to Dad's dismay I announced that I had purchased 25 laying chickens. Dad felt he had enough of chickens at work and did not want chickens on the farm. I increased the number of layers to 200 in 1961 and

maintained an egg route for 8 more years until leaving for college. During these years, other issues distracted me from my chores, especially girls. Dad would always be watching and make sure all the work was properly done even if he had to do it himself. I knew this bothered him, but he rarely complained. Dad and I worked together on many projects at the Fahm. One of the biggest was building a fallout shelter in 1961. President Kennedy had suggested building shelters and my father, always putting his family's safety first, sent away for plans. We spent any spare time that winter digging out more of the cellar and building the shelter. The cellar had been only partially dug out and since the house was 200 years old, the dirt was very hard to dig. All dirt had to be removed from the cellar by wheelbarrow. At 10 years old, it was a hard task for me. My father and I also raised turkeys and before thanksgiving and Christmas we dressed the turkeys in the cellar. We spent at least 80 hours a year dressing, eviscerating, and delivering turkeys. The hardest year was 1963, as President Kennedy had been assassinated the Friday before thanksgiving and all the radio stations were broadcasting only news about the assassination. Dressing turkeys was very boring and my relief was to listen to music on the radio, and there was no relief that year.

Turkey Porches
1966

During the years 1946 to 1970, Dad continued working for the Cooperative Extension as Poultry Extension Specialist. His nights and weekends were mostly spent on the farm and buildings. Starting in 1967, Dad began having severe pain in his knees. The first doctor said his teeth were infecting him and he should have them removed. The second doctor said he had arthritis in his knees and began treatment, including steroids and gold shots. In 1970 he could hardly walk so he retired. In 1971, his seventh doctor said his teeth were the problem and it was the first time two doctors had said the same thing, so he had his teeth removed. He improved greatly. In 1996 under my care I finally took Dad to have x-rays of his knees (probably the first ever done), and we found that he had never had knee problems. His knees were in great condition but his hips were terrible and the pain was translocating to his knees. He was in no shape to have his hips replaced by this time due to his Alzheimer's. But finally everything made sense. In the mid-1960's, his older sister was one of three people chosen to have the first hip replacement surgeries in the US. When Dad retired early he was given half salary as his retirement income. Within 6 months the retirement program was changed that he would get 2/3 salary. With cost of living raises, he made as much as full salary after two years. This was a sum of about $11,000.00. Being a federal program tied to congress, it continued to improve to a point where, when he died in January 1997, he was making over 4 times as much as when he retired. Hooray congress. This retirement income allowed Dad to continue and grow the farming without having to worry about profit. As the strawberry crop and raspberry crop were expanded, so were the Christmas trees.

Dad was a people person. One of his favorite adventures was making and selling omelets at the state fairs in the Poultry Association Booth. He particularly liked when the booth was located next to a pizza booth, as he relished selling more omelets than they did pizza. According to Dad, many pizza booths complained and were moved because they did not relish the competition. Dad had a great rapport with the poultry men he dealt with throughout the state. A lot of these people became friends. The saddest I ever saw my dad was when the cholesterol scare happened. When the media reported that eggs were bad for people due to high cholesterol, it devastated the egg industry. One day during this time I noticed dad sitting at the kitchen table, close to tears. I asked him what was wrong and he said" I am watching my friends going bankrupt and I can't help". He did his best to do what he could including eating two eggs every morning. He knew eggs were not bad for people.

One of my first memories of Dad was him coming into the house dusty and dirty after plowing a neighbor's field well after sundown. He had gone out with our old sway-backed horse 'Harry' after he got home from work. He had done this as a favor to the neighbor. He was tired, hungry, dirty, but happy. I could see the sense of accomplishment on his face. I puzzled why he had done this as the neighbor was a grouch. It seemed to come natural to Dad. In later years, I plowed this neighbor's fields by tractor. I always charged him. Other older neighbors, when they could not farm, lamented if their fields were not mowed in late summer to keep the fields in shape and the brush from intruding. Dad and I would charge them a reasonable fee. One neighbor's field was so rocky that we almost always broke something on the tractor. When I asked my Dad why we continue to mow those fields, he told me that it was because the neighbor would feel terrible if they were not mowed. When my maternal grandfather Brown could not mow his fields and that greatly disturbed my grandfather, Dad used my 1 ½ ton Model AA platform truck to haul our 1952 Farmall Cub tractor to his farm and Dad mowed his fields. The 90 mile trip would take about 4 hours as the truck was weak on hills and overheated often. After two years of this, the motor in the Model AA was shot. Dad arranged for a neighbor to mow the fields after that.

Dad had a saying for kids who tended to get in trouble. He would say "they have character". My first recollection of him using this phrase was when my cousin started a fire in a closet at their house. Shortly after the fire department put the fire out, keeping it from any major damage, my maternal grandparents Brown had arrived at my cousin's house for a visit. My cousin who had started the fire ran out to greet the grandparents yelling "Big Fire, Big Fire". This story was retold by my father often. He always ended the story saying my cousin "Had Character". I suspect this came as a result of his own childhood. My cousin currently owns the house he almost burned down. Dad's older brother told me many stories, always including how Dad had rolled over the family car (a model T pickup) shortly after they had purchased it.

Dad had taken it out through a field without permission and had no idea how to drive. Dad also always advocated for the underdog. When a 16 year old friend from school had gotten into trouble and was being kicked out of his mother's house, Dad told me to make sure this friend knew he could come stay with us. My mother was shocked, mainly concerned about what other people would think. Dad told her that he didn't care what others thought. My friend wound up in a room in a neighboring city, paid for by his father, who didn't want him either. I have always remembered this story and my Dad's "Goodness". Dad was also always a gentle man with animals. He had grown up believing animals stay outside and humans inside. When my siblings and I were young, we always snuck cats in to the house. I believe he knew but pretended not to know. In later years it was hilarious as any cats we had that spent a lot of time in the house would often jump in his lap. The first personal softening of this outside rule for dogs was on cold nights he would bring his dog into the cellar. After my mother passed, he began bringing the dog into the house at night for companionship.

In 1961 at 10 years old, I saved my money all summer towards a go-kart. In September I had enough money and told dad that I was ready to buy the go-kart. He said "have you considered a horse".' I had not, but the thought enthused me. Dad and I found a horse named "Chubby", fresh out of a summer riding camp, skin and bones from working hard and not being well fed. He was also quite old. My brothers called him "stumble-bum". He had a trick that when you tried to get him to go faster, he would stumble, scaring you. In this method he could keep from working too hard. My brothers and Dad worked to get him to stop this, but he was stubborn. One day I was going under a tree and I reached out and broke off a small branch. Chubby saw this switch and immediately started to gallop. He never used his stumble again. Chubby was part Morgan and once he was fed well, he filled out nicely. My grandfather Brown, upon seeing Chubby said he thought Chubby was big enough to drive. He brought me a driving harness from his barn and dad and I bought an old used buggy and a sleigh that needed repair. Chubby loved to drive. Many times while driving the buggy on Route 4, me with a straw hat and a corn cob pipe, people would slow down to take pictures or movies. I have never seen any of these pictures or movies but I can still visualize them being taken.

Chubby and Buggy:
Aunt Jean, Randy,
and Toffee

The next spring, my grandfather Brown told me he thought Chubby could work. He brought me a work harness and we began using Chubby to cultivate, rake hay and occasionally plow ground. I say occasionally because Chubby did not like plowing ground, it was too hard work. Dad used Chubby for working for about 7 or 8 years until Chubby was too old. Dad much preferred working with Chubby to using a tractor. In early 1972, Dad called me to ask if it was okay to put Chubby down. Chubby was old, seemed to be in pain, and if he laid down in the pasture, he could not get up without Dad helping him. Dad and Mom were going to Fla for a few weeks (where I currently was living) and they had an 80 year old woman watching the farm. Dad was afraid that if Chubby laid down, that the lady could not help Chubby up. On the phone, I could hear the sadness in his voice. Of course I said yes and that was the last horse on the farm.

During Christmas tree season, Dad would wear red overalls and a red hat. People would look for him as they always enjoyed talking with him. It became an enjoyable part of the outing for many people. He was missed when he could no longer participate.

Dad also had an ability to read people well. He seemed to know who to trust and who not to. One friend of mine dad constantly warned me about. I could not see it, but this friend never looked adults in the eye. Dad said not to trust people who could not look others in the eye. A few times this warning kept me out of trouble as I refused to go places or do things with this friend. After a lot of trouble, this friend committed suicide. Not often but once in a while, a customer would get Dad's attention. Usually Dad would catch them attempting to steal something or do something wrong. He usually gave these people another chance. Some became good friends of Dad's. We had one customer we caught stealing from our roadside self-service stand. My brothers and their friends had a talk with this gentleman. He stayed away from the Fahm. Years later we heard he was bragging about walking in to the Christmas tree patch from another road and stealing a tree. There was about two feet of snow and he had to drag the tree about ½ mile. Dad said that if he needed a tree that bad and had asked, that Dad would have given him a free tree. This got back to the person and he stopped bragging.

Dad had a lot of patience with boys and men hired to help on the Fahm. He always hired a few extra helpers during spring vacation to help plant the new strawberry fields. One year a new boy was shown how to plant the plants and left alone to plant for a few hours. When Dad checked on him, Dad was very happy with his planting speed until realizing that all plants were planted upside down. Dad thought it was one of the funniest things he had seen. After that he always told strawberry planters that brown (roots) goes down. Dad's favorite saying about boys working on the Fahm was, "One boy is a boy, two boys are ½ a boy, three boys are no boys at all." He fully expected that the more boys he put on a project, the slower the work.

Barn in Winter: photo by Heather Warren

My wife called the barn, the "megabucks" barn. She said if she hit the megabucks, she would have the barn rebuilt and use it for barn dances and meetings. Although sturdy, the barn was a disaster. In 1946, shortly after purchasing the Fahm, Dad and Uncle John repaired the roof which had partially caved in. They used the floor boards for the roof boards, removing most of the floor and leaving the upright timbers resting on rocks. Over the next 10 years, Dad worked on jacking the walls and cementing a new foundation. When he was low on funds, he would make the cement go further by using it more like grout between rocks rather than concrete. One bag on the north wall went 15 feet at his stingiest. Over the years, we made horse stalls, poultry pens and storage rooms in the barn. In the early 80's Dad had his right hand man, Dick, start cementing the areas below the interior upright beams, replacing the rocks used from the 1946 changes. Dick worked many years for Dad. They were great friends also. Dick was a very hard worker with little or no common sense. When operating a tractor, he could break things better than any employee before or after. Well neither Dick nor Dad was an engineer. They just jacked the beams, cemented under them and put them back down. They eyeballed the height. And "OOPS", one beam was left about 1 foot too high. Over the next two years the barn shifted around this beam. Dad, oblivious to why this was happening, braced and re-braced the barn as timbers moved. This resulted in an obviously tilted structure, braced and strong in its new position. The new owners plan to dismantle the barn and rebuild it correctly.

Mid way through June 1996, Dad passed out in his rose garden. When we got to him, it appeared he was snoring. After an ambulance ride and stay in the hospital, no cause was found. In hindsight, we realized he never slept again more than a brief few minutes. Not knowing what was going on, we tried in vain to aid him in sleeping to no avail. His Alzheimer's was progressing and the next 6 months were very difficult. When his prostate stopped working, the resulting pain kept him from walking for a few days and he never learned to walk again. With his lack of sleeping, and his mental state, 24 hour care was necessary. For the rest of the summer and into the fall either Heather or I tended Dad, the

other tended customers, and nobody tended the fields. I had
made a promise to him that I would keep him at the Fahm as long
as possible and when in October 1996 he went into hospital care
and then to a nursing home, he did not know he owned a farm.
Although with great help from Heather and others, I am proud
that I kept that promise.

Dad, Denny and Ann
at Our Wedding
7/22/90

Dad loved interacting with customers at the Fahm and always
greeted people with a big smile. He taught me that the "Biggest
Asset" at the Fahm was our customers. I often said that no ear of
corn or Christmas tree ever paid me. People often told us how
seeing Dad always brightened their day. In the grip of
Alzheimer's, Dad still would greet people the same way. Late
summer 1996, we would let Dad sit outside where he could
interact with customers. Quite a few times, the following exchange
would happen. A customer would approach us and ask how Dad
was doing. We would tell them that he had very little memory.
They would go talk to Dad. He would greet them with a big smile
and say things like "great to see you" or "how have you been", or
"how is the family". They would brighten up, have a conversation

and stop by to tell us that Dad wasn't that bad and that he had remembered them. After they left, Dad would ask "who was that". We would tell him and his next question was usually "am I supposed to know them".

Dad and Geese: photo by Peter Whitson Warren

Chapter 6: Growing Up on the Fahm

A lot of parents treat their children the opposite of how they were treated by their parents. Both my mother and father were raised in the traditional family structure that the father rules and the mother takes care of the house and children. My grandmothers were stay at home Mom's. My mother followed in this path but in possible reaction to how strict their fathers were, my parents were not strict at all. My parents gave my siblings and myself great freedom. We were given freedoms earlier than my friends. My parents were very loving and caring to a fault. I learned not to ask for permission to go someplace or do something, I just told them what I was going to do. My parents were very loving to each other. I believe my mother's greatest love was my father. My father's greatest love was the Fahm, followed very closely by his love for my mother. This enabled him to be okay after my mother passed.

My two brothers were 7 and 10 years older so I got to watch but rarely participate with them. They were allowed immense freedom and this allowed my sister who is 3 years older than myself and I to enjoy a level of freedom that was rare in its day and even rarer today. We could tell our parents we were leaving on our bike and travel miles to any destination. I rode my bike to school on occasion, a 10 mile trip each way. As teenagers, we hitch-hiked often. We were allowed to date and to make-out which amused our friends. I was told at 10 years old, that if I wished to smoke cigarettes, I could smoke in front of my parents. This did come from a level of fear that if I hid in the barn to smoke, I might burn the barn down. My brothers had been caught smoking in the barn. My parents would take us to friends' houses, roller skating rinks or movies almost every time we asked. When I made decisions even at 9 yrs. old (bought chickens) our parents would allow it. My sister was allowed to not work on the Fahm and to work on her tan instead if that is what she wanted. As I reached mid-teens, I became obsessed with girls, money, and cars. My money making ventures on the Fahm were supported by my parents. This usually meant my father helping because I did not always keep up as I should. My friends would stay over often and during one two year spell, my friend Ross spent about as much time at my house as he did at his own.

Our road from Route 4 was 1/3 mile long. Throughout school, we had to walk to the Route 4 end of the road to wait for the school bus. My brother Bradley and sister Ann were with me when I started. Entering second grade, it was Ann and I. By the time I entered sixth grade, I was alone. At the end of the school day, we were dropped off at the end of the road and walked to the house. Sometimes my sister went to friends or had been ill and I would walk alone. This was normal and I actually liked this. Today this would not happen. A few times our bus would break down or get stuck in snow on Hall Rd. The bus driver would have us walk to the next road to wait for another bus (after it had completed its own route) as our bus would be blocking the narrow road. We would be happy to get to school late. We could not wait for it to happen again. If a fellow bus rider was too unruly, he or she would be put off the bus wherever we were, and told to walk home. If a friend came to my house after school, he just got on my bus.

My obsession with cars started in 1961 when a friend of the family offered to sell his 1952 Chevrolet pickup to me for $25.00. It was rusted to a point it would not pass inspection but ran well. A friend and I had taken a horseback ride after school out through the woods. When we returned to the house, the truck had been dropped off and the keys were in the ignition. I told my friend to get in, and I proceeded to scare him quite well as I learned to drive. Fast was best. My brothers had a field where they had a spinout track. My friend screamed as I spun the truck around the track. I can still remember the thrill of scaring my friend. My brothers had numerous farm vehicles with the most notable a 1946 Plymouth convertible. One summer my parents, sister and I took a trip and upon returning found four of the large sugar maple trees in the yard damaged about 18 inches up from the ground. The '46 Plymouth now had a v shaped front end where the car had been rammed repeatedly into the trees. They also repeatedly zoomed down the road, putting the car into reverse and popping the clutch. Eventually that car's transmission was ruined. Another story goes: Bradley was driving toward the farmhouse with flames shooting out of the engine of a '37 Chevrolet pickup. The car had no hood. The flames were shooting above the car and Bradley was oblivious to the fire. My mother ran out to stop him and he misunderstood and waved back to her. Finally he saw the flames, stopped and used a little sand to put the carburetor fire out. After my first vehicle, I owned a succession of farm vehicles. The list includes, 1951 Chevrolet sedan, 1957 Chevrolet sedan, 1950 Plymouth sedan, 1947 Dodge 1 ½ ton dump truck, 1956 Mercury sedan, 1950 Ford pickup, and 1960 International Harvester Travelall. All these were owned between 1962 and 1969. Most were purchased at the local junkyard except for the 1950 Plymouth sedan and 1950 Ford pickup which were gifts from neighbors. All were rusted and were not road worthy. In 1967 when I got my first license, I had a 1957 Chevrolet sedan and a 1931 Model AA 1 ton platform truck to drive on the road. My friends enjoyed coming to the farm and driving around the fields. The dirt road was always wash boarded just out of sight of the house where we would "hit it". The farm vehicles were used to service the self-service stand during the summer. The stand was definitely checked more often due to the fun of driving.

I was obsessed with the desire to get my driver's license. New Hampshire required completion of a Driver's Education course and you could not start the course until you were 16 years old. I did not have public transportation to school so I called the local Juvenile Officer in Dover and asked for permission to take the Drivers Ed course early. He allowed this except he said I could not do the 6 hours of on road driving until I was 16. These courses were through private individuals. My Driver's Ed instructor was an insurance agent. I completed the classroom and written part of the course and on the morning of my birthday the instructor picked me up at 6:30 am. We drove for the next 6 hours as I took him to various appointments for his insurance company. We even went to one appointment in Massachusetts where I could not legally drive even as a student. Coming back into NH we approached a toll booth and I had to wake him up for money for the toll. I thus completed my driving portion of the course. That afternoon, my Mom and I drove to the DMV in Dover where the one person for our area gave driving exams. Mr Redden greeted me with the statement, "It's about time you drove legally". He was a customer of the Fahm and knew I drove on the Warren Rd. I passed the written exam and he and I got into our car. We drove out of the DMV and he said turn right. We turned right three more times as he took me around the block back to the DMV. I was relieved that he did not ask me to parallel park. On my 16th birthday I had my license. My '57 chevy and '31 Model AA 1 ½ ton Platform truck were already registered and inspected. I had become mobile.

Years later, my son Earl would follow in the same footprints, changed to reflect the changing times. He learned to drive on the Fahm and Warren Rd. He wowed the driving exam person at the DMV when he took his test. And he was allowed the freedom the Fahm allowed.

Farmhouse with Beauty Bush in Full Bloom: photo by Heather Warren

Chapter 7: Summer of 1989

Early in 1989, I was employed as a third shift supervisor at a plastic bottle making plant in southern New Hampshire. I was well paid and had great benefits which included health insurance, paid holidays and paid vacation. It was the job I wanted. I was a weekend Dad and my three children usually came to stay with me every other Saturday morning and went back to their respective mother's on Sunday evening. As the spring progressed, my father was having troubles accomplishing the spring work at the Fahm. Dad's right hand man had a heart problem and could not work. Dad, who usually could work more when needed, was slowed by his age. He was 77. Dad, usually a very positive, upbeat person, was showing the stress and disappointment of falling behind in the farm work. I would try to go to the Fahm, to help with the work, on the weekend that I did not have my children. It was obvious that my limited help was not slowing the trend of falling further behind. I did not want to leave my job but I could not see any alternative. In May I gave my notice at work. Upon telling my father that I was leaving my job, he leaned across the kitchen table and with a look of desperation asked me "When can you start?" I had left this plastics plant once before and knew that I would not be eligible to return. My plan was to spend the summer catching up the farm and in the fall I would go find another job, as there was not enough income at the farm to provide for year-round employment. Thus I gave up my benefits and reduced my pay and began my tenure as the steward of the Warren Farm. It was 24 years before "my summer" ended.

Chapter 8: Christmas Trees

Christmas trees have been the hallmark of the Fahm since 1957. It was also Dad's favorite and steadiest crop. While healthy, he loved to pick up a scythe to cut brush and weeds in the patch. Dad always preferred hand tools to machinery. While working at UNH, he would get home in the afternoon change his clothes and pick up a hoe or scythe to work in a field. If you went out to see him, he would often tell you, "This is heaven". If you gave me a hoe or a scythe, I would think "This is Hell". The customers during the Christmas tree season were the most upbeat. In the 70's and 80's many people saw the number of customers at Christmas tree farms on a weekend day. They believed that they could take their land, plant it to Christmas trees, and get rich. Many acres of trees were planted only for the owners to find that the work was much greater than they thought. Thus there are many overgrown Christmas tree fields in southern NH. Some did the work and flooded the market. Our best year through the 70's 80's and 90's was 1987. Dad had expanded the fields of trees and they looked great. Sales were at a new record. In 1988, 10 new Christmas tree farms started selling trees within 20 miles of our farm and our sales were cut in half. One of the 10 was still in business by 1998. It is always surprising what details influence others. In the late 70's a bug called the "fir midge" damaged the Balsam Firs throughout our area. The midge would lay its eggs in the base of the needles and if you cut the tree and brought it indoors, the needles would fall off within a few days. There was no known remedy and Dad decided to stop growing Balsams. He switched to Fraser Fir and Blue Spruce. We became known for our Blue Spruce. We gave Fraser Fir the nickname "deer candy" as the deer would eat the buds as high as they could reach during the winter and early spring. Thus we grew some really ugly Fraser's. The fir midge was cyclical and never has been a problem again.

When I returned to the Fahm in 1989, I planted the Balsam Fir seedlings that dad had heeled in years earlier and re-introduced Balsams to the farm. Dad had tried Concolor Fir, but he had planted them in wet ground believing that was best. During the 1995 drought, they grew tremendously, teaching us that they needed dry ground. Again Mother Nature taught us a lesson. To this day my biggest regret once I controlled the Fahm, is that I didn't plant the whole farm to Christmas trees. My father often stated that this was his biggest regret also.

Back Christmas Tree Patch: photo by Heather Warren

My first involvement with the Christmas trees began in 1960. I would greet the customer after they parked in front of the farm house. I then would carry the hand saw and walk with them out to the Christmas tree patch. In 1960 we were still getting $1.00 per tree. For my part in the process, I would get 25 cents per tree.

While they looked for the perfect tree, I trudged behind them. Once a tree was selected, sometimes a lengthy process, I would cut the tree down and drag the tree the approximately 1000 feet to their car. At least this is how it was supposed to work. In reality, if one of the customers was a man, they would have to cut the tree down but would never help me carry the saw or drag the tree. If the customers were all women, they would help carry the saw, help drag the tree but would never cut the tree. As you visualize this, please remember that I was 9 years old. Our first female customer who cut their own tree was in 1968. I can still picture her determination when she told me that she would cut the tree. I was shocked but from her look, I knew not to question her. Looking back on this event, I believe that this was real progress. By 1990, it was rare for a female or male customer not to want to cut the tree themselves.

During my tenure as manager and owner of the Fahm, the roads and parking lots for the Christmas trees were constant issues. It was common for us to have a ground freeze in late November followed by rain or warmth in early December. Our road from Route 4 to the farm house was in great shape, but the road from the house to the patches had spots that were always questionable when wet. The back road had one soft low spot and the parking lot sometimes was more suited for mud wrestling than parking a car. We had one year where it rained every weekend. Each Monday I would call for at least one dump truck load of gravel to get the parking usable again. The third weekend in December it was predicted to rain heavily also. Our sales were way down due to the weather. Saturday it poured all day. We had one of the biggest days ever as customers gave up waiting for dry weather and came despite the rain. The parking lot was the worst ever. Sunday turned out to be beautiful as the forecasters had been wrong. We had an average crowd, as most customers had come Saturday.

Customers had come one day early! In the mid 2000's, we had a day where the frost came out of the ground and it also rained early in the day. Our road to our back patch became impassable by noon and our front patch parking lot was the same. I had a fellow farmer named Andre helping me in the front patch. The situation became more and more unmanageable so I had him stop all customers and have them park in our farm stand parking field, asking them to walk to the patches. I would then transport the customer's trees from the fields to their cars on one of our tractors. He was livid that I was asking him to confront the customers as he felt that they would be mad to be imposed upon this way. Within a half hour of this new arrangement, Andre was beaming, repeatedly telling how wonderful our customers were. Instead of being mad, they all asked if they could help! We had a wonderful afternoon. A few years later, we had a new west field ready for cutting and the road became easily muddy. One Saturday the road became terribly muddy and many customers were angry about how muddy their cars were getting. Adding to the dilemma was that the road was also too muddy to walk. I had a set of forks for the back of one tractor. I put a piece of plywood

 and some cushions over the forks and offered our customers a ride if they wished. I truly believed that most would not like this ride. I was pleasantly surprised when, not only did they like this, they said it was great. It was different and memorable. We had a great day again. This led to giving wagon rides starting the next year, because we could not afford to upgrade this road enough to insure it would stay passable. For peace of mind we looked to buy a wagon. When discussing this

with Bill and Brad, the managers of Emery Farm in Durham NH, they offered one of their wagons for us to try. They used their wagons for pumpkin season but not for Christmas tree season. It worked so well we continued borrowing a wagon each year. This is typical of how fellow farmers work together. This borrowing of a wagon made it great for the years until we sold the Fahm.

During our Christmas tree season, we would cut a few trees and offer them as discount trees. This began when Dad realized that some people could not afford a full price tree. This pre-cut tree patch became a tradition at the Fahm. Those people wanting a small tree, cheaper tree, outside bird tree, or second tree would usually find one in the discount tree lot. We had some environmentally minded customers who did not want to cut a tree. These people for some reason felt it was okay if the tree was already cut. These trees usually came from areas we wanted to clean out or thin. By 2012, 1 of out every 5 trees we sold were from our cut tree patch. We also offered a bough pile for customers to use for wreaths or decorating. This pile was from our trimmings and junk trees. It became so popular that it took a lot of effort to keep the pile full. In the early 2000's Heather began making Christmas Wreaths. We bought a wreath machine and a clamp machine. She sold over 200 wreaths made on the wreath machine the first year. The next year she was so busy with dried flower wreaths that she had no time to make Christmas wreaths. I began making wreaths on the clamp machine and found I made a great wreath and I liked doing it. Through our tenure on the Fahm, we sold around 200 wreaths each year except the ice storm year of 2008. I truly enjoyed making wreaths and Heather would decorate some with bows, pine cones, cedar sprigs, winter berries and various other decorations. We were quite the Christmas Wreath team. Our wreaths were made fresh and became known by some as "Mother's Day" wreaths as that was when they would start to dry out.

We did, at times, have organizations ask for donations of our goods so they could compete with us. One particular year a business organization in town called and asked if we would donate the materials so they could raise money by giving Christmas wreath making classes. They intended to charge well for these classes and hoped for a large number of customers. Wreaths had become a significant sales income during Christmas tree season for us. Most of the people in this organization were our customers. I stated back to this person making the request that in other words you want me to donate my materials, to make my products, to sell to my customers. She said "Wow I didn't think of that".

Wreaths 2011: Photo courtesy of Scott Young

Chapter 9: Strawberries and Raspberries

In the late 50's I took over the Fahm as Peter and Bradley grew older and turned to other interests. By 1960, at the age of 9, I became the primary strawberry and raspberry picker at the Fahm. According to my records, I picked and sold 256 quarts of strawberries and 827 pints of raspberries in 1960. By 1967 before we began pick your own, I picked 2241 quarts of strawberries and 1580 pints of raspberries. My biggest helper during these years was my Grandfather Milford Brown. When I could not keep up with the berries, my mother would call him and he would arrive to help for a few days. He was the fastest strawberry picker I had ever seen. Occasionally I would ask how he could pick so fast and his answer was always the same. He would say the trick to filling a quart basket quickly was to place a rock in the bottom. I always worried that a customer would come tell us a rock was in their basket of berries. My sister, Ann spent a little time helping the farming operation, but she had little interest. I increased the size of the strawberry beds as well as the corn fields to a point in 1968 where I could no longer pick all the strawberries. I asked some of my friends from Oyster River High School to help. The first day it went great. The next day also went well, but I made the mistake of paying them. They did not show up for work the third day! Desperate to keep up with the berries, I offered the regular customers half price to pick their own berries. This worked so well that by 1970, the strawberry and raspberry crops were 100% pick your own.

Our first two pick your own customers were the Grays and the Nichols. They lived next to each other on a busy highway and were retired. They would pick berries daily and sell them on their front lawns. They would price gouge each other and competed in every way possible, including watching the other to make sure they would not get a head start on them. They each tried to be the first in the field in the morning. Dad would check the fields each morning to see if he had enough ripe berries to be open to pickers. He would then answer the phone to tell people if he was open. One morning he knew from how the fields looked the night before that he would probably be closed. He had always let the Grays and Nichols start picking whenever they arrived, but it was 4:30 am. Both couples were in the field picking already. Dad was quite upset and when he went to talk to them, they complained that the picking was poor as there were not enough ripe berries. This was enough for Dad and the policy of no people in the fields before the opening time began that day. One of my favorite customer stories (we heard a lot of them) was how Curly Nichols would tell how he had bought a table saw and the first time he used it he cut off two fingers. He would continue that when healed he tried to use the saw again and cut off the next two fingers. Then he would hold up his left hand which had a thumb and four stubs. His wife would then add that they sold the saw. Both couples became good friends of ours for years.

Parking for Strawberry Pickers 1992

Strawberry Pickers 1994

Pick your own strawberries was the rollercoaster crop of the farm. Once we became primarily PYO in 1970, we became well known for our strawberries. There were a lot of PYO strawberry farms in our area by the mid 1970's. One time another farmer called Dad asking him to band together with the other strawberry farmers to ban kids from the fields. After thinking about it for a day, he told me "I think when I ban kids from my fields, I will stop farming." Kids were always welcome at the Fahm. A few farmers banned kids and it did not go over well.

Throughout the 70's and 80's the crop fluctuated with the weather as customers were not an issue. In 1978, after a particularly wet spring, Dad had the experts from UNH look at his plants as they were doing poorly. The experts diagnosed "red steele" root disease and told Dad to plow under the field and fumigate. He was told to get "red steele" resistant varieties. Up to this point he had used plants or runners from his existing beds. We had a variety called "catskill" that was a prolific producer. Dad had used this variety from the start. Dad followed the suggestions only to find over the next few years that it was not "red steele" and instead was black root rot. The results were that we had destroyed the Catskill variety needlessly and never were able to find as good a producer. The red steele resistant varieties were more black root rot susceptible. Thus we had made the situation worse. Not managing for root rot was one of my biggest errors in strawberry farming and continually caused problems.

By 1986, we had found that the only way customers would pick the smaller strawberries would be if they tasted great. We had tried a variety called Earlyglow and it was the sweetest berry we had found. All strawberry varieties start with the first (king) berry being big and successive berries getting smaller. Earlyglow went small quickly but people liked the sweetness so well that they would do the work to pick them. By 1988 we were growing Earlyglow almost exclusively. Our best yield ever was in 1995 when the berries ripened larger on average than any other year and filled quart boxes quickly. It was a banner year. However, our new beds for 1996 proved to be a disaster. We tried a new variety and it did not like the snow cover from November 15 until spring. The snow prevented the ground from freezing, allowing root rot to multiply all winter. When the mulch was removed in the spring, the plants looked great but had no roots. Within 48 hours of the uncovering, all the plants of this variety were dead. To add insult to injury, we had a new Earlyglow bed, but the nursery we had bought the plants from had mis-labeled or made some mistake, as the berries were not Earlyglow. These were the worse tasting berries we had ever grown. The customers did not want them period! I was later to learn that the owner of the nursery had been going through a divorce and his product that year had been a problem to most of his customers.

After working with Dad's illness in 1996, Heather and I decided to spend 1997 getting our strawberry and raspberry fields back into shape. We did a great job and the strawberry crop was in the best shape it had ever been at the farm. We were ready to start picking on June 13 but it started raining on June 12 and it didn't stop. We measured 12 ½ inches of rain during the first 24 hrs. Not only the strawberry fields but all the fields had standing water in them even fields that had never had standing water before. Over the next 20 days we totaled 21 inches of rain. Even when it was not raining it was so humid that it was foggy. On Saturday, June 13 in the rain, out of desperation, I went out to pick strawberries. The strawberries were under water. While I was out picking, a man in a pickup truck dressed in a yellow rain suit pulled in. It was my friend Ben. He got out of his truck and said "Randy, I was thinking of you. Can I be of help?" I paused a moment and said lets go have a cup of coffee as this is stupid. While having the coffee at the farm house, Heather made the statement: "Our strength does not come from our strawberry fields. It comes from God, we will be okay". That was the end of trying to pick strawberries that day. Over the next week the tropical air mass that was over us was so uncomfortable that very few customers came to pick even if it wasn't raining. On Wednesday the NH Commissioner of Agriculture went on NPR and stated that if people wanted to have strawberry farms next year, they better get out there now and pick the berries that are in the farmers' fields. Either too few people heard the NPR broadcast or too few cared. It did not help at all. The first comfortable day was Saturday June 20th and we were loaded with customers. We had a hard time listening to the customers coming out of the fields stating how terrible it was that over half of the ripe berries had spoiled. Although I usually could keep up a positive attitude, I did not do well that day. I know I snapped at some of the customers. The tropical air mass persisted well into July and the raspberry beds were devastated. Root rot and cane disease killed over half the raspberry beds. It became a true disaster year. The federal government had a disaster program. They lobbied the strawberry farmers to spend the time to make out the paperwork necessary to file for disaster payments. I spent many hours completing the disaster application. The program would pay 55% of the losses to the first 55% of the crop. What happened was that so many farmers in our region applied for disaster relief that the pool of funds was divided up amongst them. With well over $12,000 of coverable damages to our strawberry crop, we received $267.00. Not worth the effort!

Another rebuild of strawberry and raspberry beds during the 1999 season and the 100 yr. drought of 1999 made it a two year disaster. From June 1999 to Sept 12 1999, we did not get measurable rainfall. Heather and I would watch radar on tv of thunderstorms coming toward Concord, NH thirty miles west of the Fahm, only to watch them dissipate or split and go around us. On July 1 the foot valve started showing at the water level in our big pond and we were forced to stop using our big pump. We put a small pump in the deepest part of the pond and set up trickle irrigation on the raspberries, grapes and vegetables to save them. This pump ran almost non-stop until the morning of sept 12 when the pond was so low we had to stop that pump also. The pump had run so long and so hot that the bearings were shot and once turned off, never ran again. It rained that afternoon. The only crop that did well during the drought was the raspberries, which only had half the beds due to 1998. Growing small fruits is a crap shoot with Mother Nature holding the ball.

Pond Almost Empty 9/12/1999

As pick your own strawberries, raspberries and grapes became popular, daycares, kindergartens, and schools began planning field trips to the Fahm. Dad enjoyed the "kiddos" as he called them. He knew that for some children, this was the first agricultural learning experience. Dad would try to blend a mix of humor and knowledge. A few of these students would, when in their teens, arrive at the Fahm looking for summer employment. Often they would still remember the facts and jokes that Dad had shared with them. Dad especially liked kindergarteners as a few days after the field trip a packet of thank-you cards would arrive. Some of these would be in child handwriting and some obviously were helped by their teachers. Some were also hilarious. As dad aged and was less involved in the farming, he remained active in these field trips. Many of the teachers were disappointed when he no longer could escort the children. During the early field trips in the 70's, Dad charged a nominal fee per child. This was a common practice at other farms and still is today. On one particular field trip, a student mentioned he was sorry his friend could not come on the field trip. Dad asked why this was so and was told by this child that his friend could not pay the fee. Dad asked the teacher if this was true and was told "Yes". Dad never charged after that. He could not allow a child to be left out after that. Heather and I continued that tradition, and although more income would have been nice, we could not allow a child to be left out either. We slept well over this decision. As farming became less and less mainstream from the 90's on, these field trips to the Fahm became more and more special to the students. It was not unusual to have a new customer come to the Fahm with their 4 or 5 year old leading the way telling their parents all about the Fahm.

A School Group on a Grape Picking Field Trip, Listening to Dad

There is a widening gap between food production knowledge and consumers. This was very evident when one lady called the farm just before Mother's Day one year. She explained to me that her father loved strawberries and she would be spending Mother's Day with her father and thought it would be great to have fresh strawberries for her father since her mother had passed away. This was before supermarkets had strawberries throughout the year and no strawberries were available in stores. I carefully and patiently explained that the strawberry plants at our farm were in blossom and that it would be 3 to 4 weeks before we had ripe berries. When I got done explaining the strawberry schedule, she sharply told me that she wanted fresh strawberries for Mother's Day (a few days away) and that she had looked in the phone book for a strawberry farm, found our farm and she wanted to come buy ripe strawberries that weekend. Despite my insistence that there were no ripe berries to be bought that weekend, she angrily told me she wanted strawberries that weekend and hung up.

Strawberries for Sale at Farm Stand: photo by Heather Warren

Toward the end of our tenure on the Fahm, the exasperation with customers picking their own strawberries convinced me to start to pick more berries myself. We often had too many pickers or too few pickers who knew how to properly pick. Some pickers just wanted a way to entertain their children. Also many of our best pickers were now too old to bend properly. As I started to pick berries and sell them at the farm stand, I remembered how I liked to pick strawberries. This led to a few years of growing Day-Neutral varieties that produce all summer. These gave us new challenges but were also at times quite fun. I guess I had come full circle.

Bounty brings happiness and the strawberry crop's bounty gave me a few of the best days at the Fahm that were not during Christmas tree season. There was a day in 1992 that comes to mind. The volcano, Mt Pinatubo had changed the weather and our strawberry crop was the latest it had ever been. We had held off opening until berries were plentiful. I did not realize the enormity of the crop in the field and opened for the first day of the season on a Saturday. The crowd was gigantic and it was necessary for me to oversee parking. We were on our fourth row of cars in our front field when 7am allowed pickers to begin. As more people drove in, I could see that the pickers were beginning at the front of the rows and barely moving. They were filling baskets quickly. As it became apparent that we had lots of berries, the new people driving in would see the crowd and ask if they should come back another day. I had the pleasure of grinning and saying, "There are plenty of berries and it won't get any better than this." We had a record day. It was Monday before the pickers caught up with the crop. In 1995, we had not only a repeat of this surprise bounty but a record three day stretch that was the largest yield of strawberries we ever had.

I have always puzzled at people's opinions that farmers were rich. We had Church groups that would pick strawberries for festivals. We would give them a good discount and help if we could with the picking. They always were appreciative and most were extremely gracious but every once in a while we would be told "why don't you just donate the berries", or "we do not have enough volunteers, could you pick them for us at the same price". I do believe that there are a few people that think the hardest work we do is to hang the sign at the end of the road and collect money. Often at the end of the strawberry season the berries would be very small and hard to pick. We would give customers a discount due to the conditions. The next year we would have customers at the beginning of the season asking when we were going to offer the discount again. They were hoping to get the discount when the picking was excellent and easy. This became very aggravating so we rarely offered discounts.

Raspberry Beds with Irrigation: photo by Heather Warren

Chapter 10: Electric Fence and Irrigation

As Dad expanded the strawberries during the 70's, the problem of deer damage began to be a major issue. Dad did not want to shoot deer out of season but the green leaves of the strawberry plants were very tempting to the deer. The strawberry beds were heavily mulched in late November with mulch hay and throughout the winter the leaves would stay green. Unless the snow was deep enough to deter them, the deer would paw the hay off the plants and eat the leaves and crowns, diminishing the crop for the next year. Dad contacted the fish and game department and they started trying different methods of deterrence. One of their methods was stakes wrapped in cloth with a stinkum that made the whole field stink. It was some kind of animal urine. They were sure it would work. It seemed to attract more deer. After two years of attempts, Dad called them one morning to alert them to more damage and they said" Just Shoot Them". Dad not wanting to do this, tried one more method, an electric fence. It worked so well that he fenced the entire perimeter of the field crop area the next year. This fencing took a lot of work to maintain but diminished the damage for a number of years. We usually shut off the fence when customers were in the field but in the 90's the deer pressure rose to where we just left it on. We cautioned people about the fence and had warning signage. One day while I was tending the stand, a customer came up to tell me there had been a problem at the end of the field. A young boy had decided to go through the fence to pee. He had gotten to a point where he was straddling the fence when it pulsed, shocking him. He became frightened and just stood there getting popped by the fence. This customer told me that another customer had gotten him out of the fence but the boy's mother was quite upset. She was worried that the boy might have been injured. Soon, the customer who had saved the boy came to the stand. She was a dairy farmer and was very familiar with electric fencing. She retold the story telling me that despite her reassurance, the mother was quite worried. With this warning, I was prepared as the mother arrived at the stand. She retold the story of her son's adventure and very seriously asked if her son could have been permanently injured. I started to tell her that I had been popped by electric fences often, stopped, made a thinking face, and then said, "Maybe that is my problem". Her face relaxed as we both had a big laugh. By this time her son was in front of the stand playing with our dog. Dad usually wore sneakers when working around the electric fence. This was so he would not be grounded, thus avoiding the shock if he touched the fence. He loved to grab a blade of grass, grab the fence with the other hand and then touch you with the grass blade. He would roar with a big laugh when you got popped. One day in 1995, I was working in a field when the fence started jumping wildly. I looked around to see a moose had just walked thru a section of fence breaking all the wires in that section. The moose saw me and not wanting the moose to break another section, I slowly walked around the moose to get it to exit thru the unfenced end. When the moose realized I was herding it, it spooked and ran out to the road, narrowly missing a van driving in. That was the first but not the last time a moose broke the fence. By 1999, I gave up on trying to keep a perimeter fence intact because of moose damage. Usually I would fence a small area if we had deer pressure, but would vary the fence to keep the deer from getting used to it.

As the strawberry beds grew so did the need to irrigate the crop. In 1965 our area had a severe drought. Most of the local strawberry growers including the Fahm lost most of that year's crop. Dad decided to buy a small 1 hp irrigation pump, a feed pipe, and 7-30' irrigation pipes with sprinklers. He bought as much as he could afford. He set the pump up in our small farm pond and dug a trench from the house to the pump, installing an underground electric wire to power the pump. In 1966, our area experienced a second year of drought and we were the only strawberry farm in our area that had a full crop. Every year Dad would buy a few more pipes and sprinklers. As the system got bigger, he bought a bigger gas powered pump and the electric pump was retired. Starting in 1971, now that Dad was retired and the income from the strawberries was more important, Dad began using the irrigation system to provide frost control during blossom. This entails setting up irrigation for a light, even, thorough coverage of the whole strawberry field. On a cold night (that is below 35 degrees) during blossom, the pump would be turned on to cover the strawberry plants and the blossoms with a fine mist of water. The water would turn to ice and the effect would be to keep plants and blossoms from freeze damage. One problem was that if you started and the pump quit or something else happened to stop the sprinklers from working, the process would reverse in about 30 minutes and the freezing effect would be worse than if you did nothing. So once you turned the system on, you had to stay up all night and monitor it. Dad also had to refuel the gas pump during the night and he often had a lot of trouble restarting the motor. Dad never had the motor not start, but this was probably the most aggravated I ever saw him. Between the gas pump problems and the need for a bigger pond during dry years, Dad decided in 1978 to install a better system. He had a large pond dug that held a lot of water. He bought and had installed a 10hp electric pump with a new power pole and electric meter right at the pond. Thus he could now flip a switch to turn on the system and no refueling. This system and more pipe allowed Dad to increase his strawberry beds. Dad also installed underground trickle irrigation throughout the approximately two acres of raspberries to try to irrigate the crop without having the foliage wet. This system proved to be a constant problem as it did not provide enough water during severe droughts and leaks were constantly happening. After I took over management of the Fahm, I returned to overhead irrigation and above ground trickle irrigation that I could monitor easily. As we opened new fields in the early 90's for strawberries, we purchased additional irrigation pipe and could use this pump and pond to irrigate and frost protect in any field.

The irrigation system has a number of stories. It was used for frost control, watering and cooling. One day in 1987, Dad went to water a section of his strawberry fields but connected the wrong pipe and turned on the water in a field full of customers picking their own berries. He found out how fast his customers could run. In 1988, while installing the feed pipe into the pond at the start of the season, he forgot to tighten the foot valve bolts. The system started great and ran well until the first time he shut off the pump. Once off, the water pressure blew the foot valve off about 16 feet below the surface. I arrived at the farm that Sunday to find Dad and his right hand man on a hastily built raft, using a 20 foot pole to try and locate the foot valve. It was predicted to freeze that night and another foot valve could not be purchased before Monday. Without the frost control the system could provide, the strawberry crop would probably be severely damaged. So there was a sense of desperation. Once located, I volunteered to dive to retrieve the foot valve. I found out how difficult it is to dive in 40 degree water, but the foot valve was recovered. That was the closest to hypothermia I have ever been. That system is still in use at the Fahm by the new owners.

Chapter 11: Additional Crops

Grapes

Grapes were added in the early 70's and became a popular pick your own crop. Many of the grape plants came from cuttings from the family farm in Ithaca NY, now owned by Dad's sister and brother-in-law, the Hertels. The grapes were self-service for many years until lack of honesty of some customers made it unsustainable. The grape crop was carried for years by a Lebanese community in Newmarket NH who would have a member pick 100 lbs. or more daily. When this customer base disappeared, a French-Canadian community took its place for about 10 years. When this group stopped coming, the grapes became a non-profit crop. The grape crop was ended in the early 2000's when disease and pests, and the unwillingness of myself and Heather to use the level of pesticides necessary, diminished the crop to a point it was no longer viable

Sugar Snap Peas

In the early 90's, we had a small area of garden that was non-productive. When the large irrigation pond was built the bulldozer operator had put the hardpan on top of the topsoil. It would not grow anything well, including weeds and Heather needed more space for her cut your own flower beds. After reading up on how to improve the soil, I decided to sow a cover crop of peas over the whole area. I bought two types of seeds, sugar snaps and regular peas and broadcast the seed with the only intent as to improving the soil. After the peas started growing I realized we might be able to let our customers pick their own peas. My impression was that people would like regular peas, not the sugar snaps. When the crop was ready, we let customers start picking. To our surprise, only one person picked regular peas but the sugar snaps were completely picked in a few days. So began our sugar snap pea production. This crop was one of our easiest to grow and easiest to sell. The last few years on the Fahm, I picked the sugar snap peas for the farm stand and it provided a daily draw of customers and a consistent small crop.

Garlic

Both a fellow farmer and my wife told me for a few years that I should grow garlic. I balked at the idea as I did not know anything about garlic. Eventually my farmer friend, Andre, talked me into trying the crop and mentored me as how to plant, tend, harvest, store, clean, and sell garlic. We found that the taste of garlic from our soil was excellent. For the last 5 years at the Fahm, garlic was a consistent seller and profitable small crop.

Garlic to Be Dried:

photo by Heather Warren

Sweet Corn

My brothers began the sweet corn crop and people would travel long distances for our sweet corn. Customers would drive in to the Fahm even if there was corn at the self-service stand because my brothers would fresh pick their sweet corn while they waited. I was not yet big enough to farm but would keep the customer company. Sometimes my cuteness would be rewarded with a tip for me which aggravated my brothers as they had done the work. Eventually I took over the farming and continued the sweet corn. When I left the Fahm in 1970 the sweet corn was already planted for the year. The other crops were pick your own. Dad hated picking corn. He tried picking corn, pick your own corn, and hiring someone to pick it. None of these methods were successful and he no longer planted corn for sale. After returning to the Fahm in 1989 it only took a couple years before I went back into sweet corn. I found that I still knew how to pick the corn the way customers loved it. Until we sold the Fahm, it was a nice small crop

Sweet Corn: photo by Heather Warren

Vegetables

Heather and I diversified the crops during our tenure. We grew summer squash, zucchini, cucumbers, lettuce, swish chard, kale, tomatoes, sugar snap peas, sweet corn, pumpkins, gourds, winter squash, broccoli, onions, peppers, asparagus, and garlic. We found that only sweet corn, tomatoes, and sugar snap peas would get a lot of customers to drive the 1/3 mile into the Fahm. We had to have a draw. Of course, strawberries, raspberries and Christmas trees were the biggest draw. It was quite disappointing when we had an abundance of the minor crops but could not get enough customers. In retrospect, I loved having the farm stand full of various vegetables, but I am not sure it was the best management tactic. We may have taken our time away from the major crops in error.

Flowers and Soap

My wife Heather has always liked herbal products. She told me one day that she would like to make soap and I had no idea about this. When I am nervous I usually make a joke and I could envision a house full of soap as I was sure nobody would buy it. So I to started using the line "Now we will have to start taking baths around here". Heather made one batch of oatmeal lavender soap. She cut it into bars and waited for it to cure. Once it was ready for use, she put them on a cutting board next to the cash register during a busy strawberry picking day. Before the day was done, she had sold the whole batch. Once I picked my jaw off the ground, I saw that this was much different than what I had thought. Handmade Herbal Soap became a very consistent crop at the Fahm. To keep the soap dust-free in the shop was a chore as we were selling it unpackaged. Our brother-in-law Denny made a large cabinet for the soap with many pull out shelves that was still used at the Fahm. Heather made many varieties of soap and my favorite she called "Farmers Soap" after me. The largest soap sales season was Christmas tree season. Throughout the remainder of the year she built a steady customer base. She used the best oils, olive, palm, coconut, and various nut oils for super-fatting. She used all essential oils for scent except in a few cases where a particular scent had none available. Because of the quality of the soap, customers found it to be excellent for their skin. Some of the most surprising aspects of our soap sales were the many mechanics and concrete workers who swore by her soaps. We had concrete workers who whenever traveling in our area would stop and buy large quantities of soap. They said that they were always trying different soaps to help their hands from cracking and

hurting and found Heathers soaps to be the best they could find. As the soap business continued we reached a plateau of sales. We realized that to go beyond this plateau, we would have to wholesale. To wholesale, we would have to reduce our price and to do that we would have to buy inferior grade ingredients in bulk. Heather realized that this would negate the reason her soap was so good and thus she decided not to go that route. Heather still makes soap and that is good as I am totally spoiled and could not go back to regular soap.

Heather also loves flowers, both fresh and dried. At various times she grew more or less flowers dependent on her available time. She tried pick your own flowers also. It was not a consistent customer base. One of the phenomenon of flower sales was when she could not sell mason jars with a nice big bouquet in them for $5.00. She raised the price at $10.00 and sold more than at the previous price. The perception of value is an interesting concept. Dried flower and dried flower wreaths at one time were big sellers, then they went out of vogue and they rarely sold. When the demand came back, she did not have the time required. The smell of the soap and the beauty of the flowers definitely made the farm stand more inviting.

Flowers: photo by Heather Warren

Chapter 12: The Woodland

Timber and firewood were great crops on the Fahm. The land grows white pine well, also other species. When Dad bought the farm in 1946, the woods had been over harvested. By the 70's they had grown considerably. Dad decided to have a timber harvest executed in 1974, and hired a consulting forester to oversee the operation. Hemlock, pine, and red oak were in demand. Dad and his forester decided to do a cut where trees over a certain diameter would be harvested without any areas being overly cut. Twelve inches was decided as the size. A logger was contracted and the cutting began. Dad watched as his forest was decimated, roads were destroyed, and a mess was made. Three times Dad threw the crew off the land before he threw them off permanently. He vowed never to use a forester again as the forester's job was to oversee the operation. The one positive of this logging is that for the first time Dad and Mom had enough money for a savings account and taking winter vacations other than camping. Dad began an effort to clean up the woods as tops were hung in other trees and it was a mess. New woods roads were built. Firewood was becoming popular again and he sold a lot of the mess to people with pickups and a chainsaw. When I returned to NH in late 1975, it was still a mess and in my spare time I started cutting and selling firewood. From 1975 to 1982 I cut over 2000 cords of firewood, sometimes full time and sometimes part time. In 1977 I started doing improvement thinnings to obtain the firewood. In 1981 dad came to me and told me that he had hired a new consulting forester. I questioned why he would do such a thing, and he said "He is just out of college, and can't be any worse than the last guy". When I returned to the farm in 1989, I began to oversee the woodland as well as have more land cleared for crops. Charlie Moreno, our consulting forester, became a good friend and remained our consulting forester throughout our tenure on he Fahm. An improved network of woods roads were built on the arm and still exist. In the mid 2000's, a video was being done on he Great Bay Watershed by a research group and our woods roads were chosen as the example of doing it right. Numerous thinnings were done in the forest and other than damage done by drought and gypsy moths on our red oaks in the mid 90's the forest continued to improve. In 2006, after the "Mother's Day Floods" had damaged more crops, we were forced to have another large timber cut to fund the Fahm. Again the woods to the rescue. From 2006 to August 2013 when we sold the farm, the woods became integral in our financial survival. Firewood also became a crop again in the last few years. Our son Earl became the crewmember who helped us with the firewood.

When possible during the time from 1975 to 1982, after finishing cutting firewood for the day, I would take a hike in the woods. By the 90's, I knew the woodland by heart. Actually my favorite place to be on the Fahm was in the woods. Whenever possible, I would give friends or family members a tour of the woods roads when drivable. And whenever agitated or fearful, a ride through the woods by truck or tractor always helped.

Woods Road: photo by Heather Warren

Chapter: 13: Wildlife

    Woodchucks, deer, porcupines, fisher cats, foxes, raccoons, squirrels, chipmunks, birds, snakes, moose, and rabbits lived on the Fahm. In 1995, turkeys were reintroduced to the region. In 1995, the first coyotes arrived. In the early 2000's bobcats began to be seen. Dad always managed the land and crops with the concept of being in harmony with nature. When deer became a big problem in the strawberry fields in 1970's, he often threatened the Fish and Game officials that he would shoot the deer, but this was only to get the officials to work harder on the problem. He was not a hunter. The end result was to fence the fields with electric fence. This worked well until the early 1990's when moose began to reside on the land. They would walk through the fence breaking the wires. The deer would then use the break as an entrance to the field. In the 50's and 60's there was one moose in Strafford County. He was an old bull who resided in a marsh partially on the Fahm. Every year the fish and game warden would check the marsh to see if the moose was there. In 1967, he came out of the marsh in tears as the moose was obviously gone. He called me the next month elated that a moose had been spotted on Parker Mountain meaning our county had a moose again. Over the next few years many moose were seen. Many moose have been hit on roads. In 1999 we had a moose reside in a back field for the winter. Moose became regular residents. When the coyotes came in 1995, woodchucks became more manageable. Nature's harmony at work.

    Porcupines were our biggest problems in corn fields. They would push over a corn stalk, take a bite and then go to the next stalk. One year we removed 37 porcupines in a week. Years before, a bounty had been set. In the early 60's, I was told it was .25 a nose as who would want the whole body. When there was no longer a bounty the porcupines proliferated. In 1968 the far end of a corn field was being damaged. I was sure it was raccoons. About midnight one evening, I took my 22 rifle, our dog, and a flashlight and walked down beside the cornfield. I heard a chomp, chomp, chomp. I followed the sound and put my flashlight on one of the biggest porcupines I had ever seen. He looked up at me and then went right back to eating. I chased the dog back to the house and went back to the corn field. I was able to shoot three that night, but the damage kept growing. Two nights later I was in a quandary as to how to eliminate porcupines without shooting. We had been informed that a man, who was old and deranged, had wandered into the woods about 2 miles from the Fahm. The police were not sure what direction he had gone and asked everyone to avoid loud noises as they thought he was paranoid. That night I went into the cornfield hoping no porcupines were there. The first porcupine I saw made me quite concerned so I picked up a rock and proceeded to try to hit him on the nose as I had heard this would stun the animal. It worked perfectly. While stunned I took the baseball bat and hit the animal with such force I killed it. My dad had always taught me to not make an animal suffer and I have always had regard for that advice. This method worked so well that the next few nights I killed seven more. The man who was lost, was found safe in another direction from the Fahm. The only successful hunters of porcupines are fisher cats and humans. Fisher Cats roll them over and go for the belly where there are no quills.

Bear were not seen on the farm until after 2000. In the 50's and 60's, bear were not allowed to be in the area. If a bear was sighted, the police would inform Vern Chesley, an uneducated but intelligent hunter who lived with his dogs in a shack in Nottingham, NH. Vern was an expert in bear tracking. He kept hand written maps of the bear trails in our region. When Vern was notified of a bear sighting, he would check his maps. He and his

71

dogs would set out on the trail near the sighting until he saw sign of the bear. He would then sit down and wait for the bear to return, as bears (according to Vern) would always come back the same trail. The dogs would alert Vern when the bear came and Vern would shoot the bear. Then the bear would be hung from the gas station sign of the nearest gas station. The local newspaper would have a front page picture of the bear hanging at the gas station.

We often saw snakes. One incident was when I was about 6 yrs old. My sister was afraid of snakes, so when I saw a garter snake I picked it up to scare her. I threw it at her and missed. The snake wrapped around the neck of a lady visiting my mother. The adults were not pleased. In the mid 90's, while having some well piping replaced, I took the plumber into the cellar, noticed a 5 ft milk adder laying on a beam, and I waited until we got to the other end of the cellar before asking, "How are you with snakes?" As he was panicking, I suggested we leave through the other end of the cellar, avoiding the snake. He was very grateful. The adders had always done a nice job of controlling mice in the cellar.

As we opened more crop land in the early 90's, we saw an increase in birds of many species. In 1991 the beavers built a dam on neighboring land and backed up the marsh (swamp) on the eastern side of the Fahm, flooding the 30 acre marsh. The water level was raised by about 2 feet killing the trees in the meadow. It had been a mature red maple swamp or marsh. Since this area was many acres and about a third was on our Fahm, I read articles and books on how to use this area creatively. I saw an article that explained that if some dead trees were removed and some remained, the area would attract all types of water birds. In the winter of 94/95, we had enough of a freeze that we hired a logger to clear a large area of the marsh on our land, knowing that our neighbors would not do anything on their land. The duck, goose, and heron populations multiplied rapidly. A hurricane removed a lot of the trees on the neighboring land in the swamp, but cedars on the eastern side still provide heron nests. In 2005, a friend started birding on the Fahm and began a list of birds sighted. When we sold the Fahm in 2013, the list numbered 150. To attract this number of bird species, we had begun in the early 90's, clearing brush in one area every few years to keep it in early successional. Early successional is the first few years of growth after land is cleared and then allowed to regrow. Early successional habitat helps threatened snakes, insects, birds and other small animals by providing food and cover from predators. Mother Nature provides this by forest fires, wind storms, and beaver floods similar to our marsh. Man has prevented forest fires in NH and cleans up after wind storms to keep land neat. This has kept naturally occurring early successional areas from happening. Man also keeps beavers from building dams that flood land. Many threatened species are threatened because they need early successional habitat. Early successional habitat also came from abandoned pasture and cropland. By the 2000's most acreage in NH was developed or forested. Throughout the US and NH, programs were started to encourage landowners to create early successional areas. The magic number was determined to be 25 contiguous acres to accomplish habitat for many threatened species. In the late 2000's while discussing another project with our NRCS (Natural Resource Conservation Service) field agent, we mentioned how we were going to cut the brush again in an area to enhance bird habitat. She mentioned that she had money to pay for such work. Heather jokingly said sign us up. She did! Thus began a four year project that started small and kept increasing to get to the 25 acre target of early successional habitat. The primary target was for New England Cottontail rabbit, to keep that species from becoming endangered. We felt it ironic that the

Warren Farm was creating habitat for rabbits when a warren is a rabbit's home. Also my mother-in-law's maiden name is Hare.

Early Successional Area Behind House After Brush Has Been Recut 2011

A funny adventure happened in 1989. I arrived at the Fahm and sat at the kitchen table with Dad. Shortly, Charles, an older gentleman who worked at the Fahm came in very excited. He told Dad that they had caught a cat. The two of them had been trying for a week to catch a cat that had recently come to the Fahm and was fighting with the resident barn cat and stealing its food. Multiple attempts had only succeeded in catching the barn cat. Dad asked Charles if they had caught his cat again and Charles said yes. They had a great laugh. The next day upon arriving at the Fahm, I could not immediately find Dad or Charles. When I located them in the barn, they were working together to try to use a ten foot pole to open the have-a-hart trap. They had caught a different cat Charles said, one with a white stripe. They had been trying to free the skunk for a long time. I walked in to the barn, grabbed a sack, walked to the trap, threw the sack over it, carried the trap outside, opened it and I walked away. They were in shock at what I had done. I then told them, I knew a skunk would not spray in a confined space. The skunk walked out of the trap and ran to the woods. They never caught the other cat, but eventually it left on its own. Our barn cat stayed at the Fahm for years and eventually became the house cat.

Skunks were a constant concern at the Fahm. One evening I went outside to work just after dark and our new dog disappeared behind the barn. In a few minutes, a whiff of skunk was present followed by the dog slowly walking toward me. The dog had gotten a face full of skunk. Washing and tomato juice mitigated the smell but did not eliminate it. The dog was relegated to stay outside for the night. The next morning, Heather called the dog but it did not come. She checked another door and saw white fur under the door. The door had been repeatedly scratched by a previous dog to a point where it had a large area removed about 6inches high at the bottom. It had worked well as a cat door as the next door of the two door set was able to be pushed open by the cat so we had not repaired the damage. This white fur under this door looked suspiciously like a skunk. Heather called me and I went out the front door and cautiously approached the other door to find the dog had herded two pygmy goats up against this door. I had no idea where these goats had come from so I built a quick wire fence area and checked to see which goat was the leader and which the follower. I knew that if you carried the leader, the follower would follow on its own. I picked up the leader and moved it to the fenced area and the follower stayed right by us. After contacting the police we found the owners who had been looking for the goats for two days. They had traveled about two miles down the powerline corridor. The owners were very pleased! And Heather and I were pleased that these were goats not skunks.

Another story about wildlife happened in June 1995. In the evening just before dusk, our son Earl and I took a tractor ride to go scout the strawberry field. When we got close to the field there was a moose standing in the middle of the field. I drove as close as I could for my 4 year old son to see the moose. The moose left the field and I thought Earl would be impressed. He was not. Later that evening Heather looked out an upstairs window and saw what she thought was our cat playing with a bush in front of the house. Upon closer examination she saw it was a fox. We had seen this fox often hanging out with our cat when we would return home after being out in the evening. Heather called to Earl to see this fox. He was not impressed. The next morning while sitting in the kitchen, I spotted a wild turkey walking into a front corn field. I told Earl to go outside and growl real loud to scare the turkey. He did just that and it spooked the turkey. He thought that the turkey's reaction was hilarious. He always liked turkeys after that. The turkey had obviously been released from a breeding program and stayed around the house for quite a few days. Earl and our cat would stalk the turkey. The turkey would let them get close but never too close. We always wondered what would happen if the cat actually caught the turkey as the turkey was much bigger than the cat.

Having a dog on the farm became a necessity. After we had to euthanize our dog a few years before we sold the farm, we wanted to wait to get our next dog. One night my wife heard loud footsteps outside our windows, we checked the next morning and there were moose tracks between the house and an out building. We soon got another dog.

Chapter 14: The Rock and Shell House

Shell House: photo by
Heather Warren

In the early 80's Dad had his right hand man clean up the old cobbler shop. We do not know the origin or use of this small shed but it possibly could have been the blacksmith and/or cobbler shop for the Fahm. Since 1946 it had been used as a pen for a few chickens, rabbits one year, and then the pen was used to raise the small chickens and geese before putting them in larger pens or in the case of geese into the fields. After ending my egg route in 1969, it had very little use. My mother had begun collecting shells and minerals during the 70's. My parents took many trips to Florida and a few trips to Hawaii, the Bahamas and Bermuda. On all these trips my mother collected shells and minerals. She had collected china tea sets and Depression glass as well as Flow Blue china. Due to the amount of glassware and china, she did not have enough display area in the house so this shed became hers. Paneling was put on the walls and the floors were cleaned, sanded and clear-coated. This small building became a rock and shell collection house. We began calling it the Shell House. My favorite picture of my Mom is of her sitting in the Shell House. She kept her shells cleaned and tagged and was very proud of her collection. She had many books about shells and minerals also. She would give tours to anyone who wished and a few young girls became regular visitors to the Shell House when their parents were picking berries. The rocking chair my mother was sitting in when the picture was taken was bought at the contents auction held in 1997, by my mother's favorite young girl, who was now a young lady. My father had given this young lady my mother's favorite, most expensive shell, and that shell became the young lady's centerpiece of her own shell collection. After Heather and I were at the Fahm, Heather cleaned the collection but it was eventually abandoned. When we put the Fahm up for sale we sold some of the collection, gave some of the shells and minerals to young customers, and kept a selection for our own enjoyment. Whenever giving a shell or mineral to a young child, we made sure to tell them how happy my mother would be for them to enjoy it. It was fun to have the collection on display in the farm stand.

Mom in Shell House: photo by Peter Whitson Warren

Chapter 15: The Media and the Fahm.

The Fahm and its farmers have been in newspapers, radio and television. Also numerous magazine and trade publications have included quotes and pictures of the Fahm. When my parents protected the Fahm via a conservation easement, the press welcomed the chance to publish pictures and articles about it. In 1996 our local newspaper published one of its first color photos. They chose grapes for the picture. We were the only grape grower they knew so they contacted us. . They published a front page picture of me under a grape arbor holding concord grapes. Numerous times the local newspaper published articles about the Fahm. One notable time was after another newspaper had published an article called "Not Berry Good" about how the strawberry crop in NH had rotted in the fields due to excessive rains. They had heard how southern Massachusetts had lost their crop, but they were in error as our region had a bumper crop. The article kept many customers away. After a great lobbying effort and a call from Heather to the editor, our local newspaper finally published an article describing the bumper crop and lack of customers. Immediately the phone began ringing and continued for a few days both at our farm and other strawberry farms. Our fields filled with customers, but this was too late to save the season financially. In 1999, our local television station showed pictures of a raspberry field in Concord NH that had died from drought. This was one of the few farms that had no irrigation and the other farms were having a good crop. Again our local newspaper debunked the myth and this time our season was saved. In 2001, our local ABC affiliate, WMUR decided to air an extended article about grapes and strawberries. They spent half a day filming at a local vineyard and then came to the Fahm for the strawberry part of the article. The man doing the filming became enthralled with a 1948 Farmall Cub tractor parked near our grapes. He spent over 1/2 hour repeatedly filming the newswoman walking past that tractor. I showed them the tiny grape clusters starting to grow, and that also excited them. They called the next day to tell me, a longer than average 5 minute article, would be aired that night on the 6 o'clock news. That was the day Jim Jeffords, a senator from Vermont, changed parties to tip the balance of the U.S. Senate for the democrats. This took over all newscasts. The edited actual airing of the farming article was about 15 seconds of me on a tractor and the newswoman holding a grape cluster all captioned with the name of the other farm and the other farmer. He and I laughed for months. Radio ads were an important tool during the 80's and 90's. Although more expensive than newspaper ads, for quite a few years we received a big boost in customers whenever we ran ads on our local AM station. As radio stations proliferated, this payoff diminished. As FM stations began to be mainstream, we tried them as a tool, but never with good results. During the best times with the AM station, it was much faster to get a radio ad to customers than the days it took to get it in print. We also could never duplicate the customer service that we received from the AM station. If we let the DJ know we had a big need for customers, he would also give free airtime of a personal nature. When we put the Fahm up for sale in 2011 it was front page news as well as when we accepted the offer from the new owners.

Chapter 16: Pesticides

I am biased in my opinion of pesticides and will offer my opinion but the use of pesticides on the Fahm was important to its evolution. Many of the pesticides my father used in the 50's are banned today. Some of these were particularly dangerous and my Dad learned to be careful. One of our neighbors, who also grew raspberries, had a bug infestation and the local supply store suggested Guthion. This neighbor applied the Guthion without reading the label and while applying this chemical got it all over himself. Soon thereafter he began feeling poorly and read the label to see if the Guthion might be to blame. This neighbor wound up getting an ambulance ride and an extended hospital stay for pesticide poisoning. This was a great lesson for us as the person applying chemicals is usually at the most risk. Scientists are still arguing about the book and research for Silent Spring. Dad being a Poultry Scientist knew the premise was suspect due to his knowledge of calcium cycles in eggs. Regardless of what is true, when DDT was banned, farmers had to find new methods of insect control. Many times when a chemical was found to work, it was overused. Dad was always cautious and always tried to err on the side of less use, not more. As Dad aged, his last responsibility was spraying. In 1992 he went to get on the cub tractor we used for spraying, could not get on properly and fell. His legs were sore and did not work well. He went into the house and since I had seen this happen, I put a bucket by the tractor for him to use as a step. A few minutes later he attempted again to get up onto the tractor, using the bucket, but he fell again. He went back into the house. I waited about 15 minutes or so and went into the house to ask if he was okay. All he said was "I am done farming". He followed this up with "Would you like the farm"? I was shocked to hear this but quietly said yes. He said "You will have to promise me one thing". I said "sure" and he said "You will keep me here as long as you can". I agreed and am very proud that with a lot of help from Heather and others, I was able to fulfill this promise. With that exchange I took over the pesticide responsibility. I never liked spraying and wished I did not have to spray, but I never found a sign that said "Organic" that when the bugs saw the sign, they would leave and go to somebody else's field. I worked hard to find the safest chemicals for myself and my customers. I always used chemicals as a last resort except for tarnish plant bug in strawberries, Northern pine weevil in blue spruce Christmas trees, worms in sweet corn, or mold in berries. These four problems were always present and needed attention. Another local strawberry grower claimed organic status and also stated they did not use pesticides at all. Their strawberries never had tarnish plant bug (tpb) damage. I learned later that they bought conventional pesticides for tpb control every year from the same dealer as I did. They must have waved the product in a threatening manner at the bugs to get them to leave. An Organic farmer in our area tried growing sweet corn without pesticides and found he preferred to buy ours. Ours was low spray and his had too many worms. Being close to the University of New Hampshire, as the organic movement spread, we had many customers who were concerned over pesticides. A typical conversation would go like this:

Customer, "Do you use Pesticides?"

Us "Yes".

The customer would then gasp!

This happened at least a dozen times. In the late 80's and early 90's, gypsy moths infested our forests and ate the leaves off many people's favorite trees and bushes. The conversations changed to this:

Customer: "Do you use pesticides?"

Us: "Yes."

Customer: "What do use for gypsy moths and can you come spray at my house?"

As is obvious, some people believe farmers spray for no good reason but these same people want to protect their plants. This attitude was frustrating but was a good double-check as we always thought of this before spraying. I erred on the side of caution and at times encountered crop damage due to my caution. But overall this caution kept our crop safe for our family and customers. In 1999, after the monsoon of 1998, our grapes were full of disease and insect problems. I went to Heather and told her my concern that I could use enough chemicals to save the crop but then I would not be comfortable letting customers pick and eat the crop. We decided to stay on our regular spray schedule and let whatever results happen. We lost most of the crop. If I had to do it again, I would not change a thing. By the time we sold the Fahm, we used very few pesticides.

Chapter 17: Maintenance on the Fahm

One of my father's favorite sayings (and mine also), is "Farming is like ministry, It is totally based on faith and it is non-profit". Because of this reality, a farmer is also a mechanic, carpenter, plumber, electrician and accountant. Farmers can't afford to hire all work done, so the first line of defense is themselves. Dad was okay at rough carpentry, plumbing and accounting but his mechanical skills were lacking. As my brothers learned, they began to be his mechanics. I took this over later. When I started working at the Fahm full-time in 1989, my first question each day would be which tractor didn't start. Usually one or two had problems. My second question was, what did you do to try to fix them. I needed to undo whatever he had done and then fix what was needed. I tried to foolproof these tractors but was never successful. We had three International Harvester Farmall Cubs so Dad got quite familiar with their layout, but he never mastered their carburation or ignition. Dad never was an electrician and neither am I. He would hire the work done and I would do the work poorly. Our son Earl had a penchant for anything electrical and as he learned, he took over the electrical work. He laughed at my previous jobs. We never owned a welder but there was a shop about two miles up the road. I had done the welding shop owners a favor once and they were so pleased with my help that they did not charge me for a number of years. The buildings always needed upkeep and as money allowed we tackled repairs. While dad was at the Fahm, we would have him fund major repairs or upgrades. My largest project was to jack the carriage house, remove the rock foundation, and install a cement floor and new foundation. This saved the building from falling in on itself. After Dad passed, we did limited upgrades. We upgraded the "shop" where we tended customers in 1998. The shop needed windows as it was very dark. But if we were going to add windows, ve should sheetrock inner walls. If we did this we should do the ceiling and if we were going to do that we should add lights. The finished project was nice and served us well right up until we sold the Fahm. It was wonderful to have customers packed into this tiny shop during Christmas tree season. The smell of handmade soap, wreaths and hot cider made it even better. We always tried to be prudent when buying equipment on the Fahm. I found later on that I should have invested in good equipment earlier rather than later.

We did a large amount of mowing throughout the summer and fall with the most difficult being the Christmas tree fields. When mowing around Christmas trees, the stumps and rocks would show us the weakest point of any mower. A lot of time was spent repairing mowers. The decision to sell the Fahm was aided by the fact that we were getting older and beginning to fall behind on the upkeep of the buildings and equipment.

Front Field: photo by Heather Warren

Chapter 18: Life as a Farmer.

Farming is a lifestyle and one of my favorite sayings is that I only worked on the days that end in Y. When I looked out of the windows while sitting at the kitchen table, I was aware that any person driving into the Fahm would see the pretty view of the house and fields. They could see what we had accomplished, yet I usually saw what needed to be done. I made the mistake for years of making to do lists. These became for me failure lists. It worked much better when I stopped making lists except for must do's. One aspect of living on and running a family farm is that work and living was done at the same location. It is hard to get away from it. Heather always stated that she liked the view from every window and it was gorgeous. We tried to keep the appearance of the Fahm, where people arriving would be impressed. We spent a large amount of time mowing and maintaining flower beds. Numerous people called our front field Randy's Golf course. I never played golf. This appearance was pleasing to us also. When the frost alarm would go off at 2:30 am, and I had to get up to start the irrigation system knowing I was now up for the night, the appearance of the Fahm did not make it easier. Getting up at 4 am to spray a crop while the wind was calm and the bees were sleeping was exhilarating and frustrating at the same time. When we had enough help to take care of customers or we were not open, I could go back to sleep in the morning, but this wasn't the financial reality during most of our tenure on the Fahm. Since we were a Pick Your Own farm weekends were a necessity to be open. This meant that we could not go to weekend activities at other places. In the 80's and 90's Tuesday and Wednesday were our busiest pyo strawberries and raspberries day. This was because people were trying to beat the weekend rush. Weekends were not as busy. In the late 90's this shifted to where Saturday was by far the biggest as people had to work and didn't have the choice to come mid-week. When we became less pick your own during the summer, it was easier to adjust hours to be open shorter hours. Once the berry crops were finished for the year we could set regular store hours to sell our vegetables, soap, and flowers.

Our Niece Amy Returning from Field after Cutting Flowers: photo by Heather Warren

Progress

It is evident what progress did for the Fahm. I like to say I was born BC, that is before computers. Early in our tenure of the Fahm my father bought a computer for us to keep the financial bookwork. It was a DOS computer and did well and was still working in 2013 when we sold the Fahm. One example of progress was our newsletters. When we began compiling a mailing list, we would write a newsletter and take it to a print shop to make copies. Once home we would fold them, place them in envelopes, write addresses and return addresses, put stamps on them, and mail them. This process took many hours and cost about .50 each. When we began using a PC, we shortened the process by eliminating the envelopes, sealing the folded sheet of paper and printing address labels. This added a little cost but saved a lot of time. As the internet began to be popular, Heather designed and built a website for the Fahm. She had found a website designer who had built a business catering to farm websites. This became the main contact with customers as we could update the site to reflect current hours and crops at any time. In a few years we began an email list and although it took another few years, by 2007, we were able to write the letter, attach it to emails and send for no cost. I do not believe as many people read the emails as did the snail mail newsletters but it saved a lot of time and money. Whether the end result was actually progress we will never know. We advertised in the local newspapers and for years this was productive. As newspaper readership declined so did the results. Our last few years at the Fahm, we noticed a lot of new customers during Christmas tree season. We asked how they heard of us and the majority said Google sent them to our website. This was progress! From late 1968 to the present we had a sign on Route 4. My father did a lot of legwork to get this approved but it was our best advertising. Many people spent years going past that sign with some never paying attention to it. We had an expensive sign made to improve it but it was stolen. Probably it adorned a college room at UNH as Warren is a popular name. But our biggest change in visibility was when we added a MasterCard/Visa sign. We found that many people who thought we must be too small to check out realized we must be bigger if we took credit cards. The additional progress is that by 2012, 50% of customers used Credit or debit cards during Christmas tree season and many called first to make sure we did. So this was a determining factor for many.

In the early 70's a neighbor's daughter built a house on the other end of Warren Road. In the fall when the leaves had fallen, Dad saw that he could see their outside light through the trees at night. He stormed into the kitchen to tell Mom that they were moving. She firmly said "No we are not". He truly would have moved if she had agreed. He had enjoyed his privacy. Over the next 40 years a few more lights appeared. A street light on Route 4 and the lights from a house built on the front border of the Fahm across the Two Mile Road became constant. The light pollution from Dover, Durham and Rochester as well as the Lee Traffic Circle affected the previously dark star laden sky. This is the price of progress. The only times we saw that dark sky again was during power outages.

Growing up on the Fahm we were allowed freedom to go where and with whom we wished. Our friends were limited due to the distance to a friend's house. It was normal at seven years of age or older for us to ride our bicycles a mile to the little neighborhood grocery store or two miles to the traffic circle area. By the age of 12, I would occasionally ride my bike to school. We often had friends stay overnight at the Fahm. Friends changed but the freedom did not. When I went to Oyster River High School in Durham, I had no public transportation. My parents or sister would provide transportation but it was normal for me to hitch-hike if needed. People would consider the freedom we had, as child neglect today. Progress isn't always good.

View from Kitchen Sink: photo by Heather Warren

Chapter 19: A Mixture of Additional Stories

July 22, 1990

I remember this day as the most perfect weather I have ever experienced. It was an 80 degree day with puffy clouds, low humidity, and a slight breeze. It wasn't almost perfect, it was perfect.

Heather and I met in October of 1989. She and a girlfriend had the dead car battery and I had the jumper cables. A good friend Fred and I had planned a picnic at the Fahm for a large group of friends for July 22, 1990. We had a wonderful picnic at the Fahm during the summer of 1989 and wished to repeat it. Heather and I decided to get married at this picnic.

We started the day with grilled hamburgers, hot dogs, and corn on the cob. The meal began at noon. We had a gathering at 2 for a gratitude discussion. At 4pm Heather and I were married under the two big sugar maple trees behind the house. As would be expected, the day had become about the wedding. We had about two hundred friends and family in attendance. Throughout the day, the attendees walked around the Fahm, nibbled on ripe raspberries, and experienced the Fahm's beauty.

The Fahm proved to be an excellent venue for a wedding or for any event.

Our Wedding

Our good friend Al took a video throughout the day and presented us with an edited copy a few days later. It was heartwarming to see the relaxed atmosphere everyone had. During the nuptials, Al panned the camera to catch the people walking around, others swinging on a swing set, our son Richard sitting on a soccer ball, and the many people in an assortment of lawn chairs.

Our niece Kirstin had the pleasure of having the Fahm be her venue when she married Ken in August, 2008. Another gorgeous day and the Fahm proved to be an excellent venue.

Ken Took the Leap

Kirstin and Ken 8/23/2008

Kirstin and Ken's Wedding Tent

Our friends Mike and Betsi also took advantage of the Fahm in October of 2008 for their wedding.

Betsi, Mike, Heather, and Randy

Ice Storm of '08

One of the extreme weather events was the ice storm of '08. We were about half way through the Christmas tree season and it was going well. It started raining and freezing on the trees. It did not stop as ice accumulated. The power went out and during the night we heard loud crashes but could not see the damage. Branches were breaking off trees and we hoped the damage would not be too great. In the morning, we found that a lot of trees had severe damage but luckily the major branches had missed the buildings. The shell house had a minor hit. What we could not see was the devastation to the Christmas tree season. The next day we were able to borrow a generator to get water and keep the refrigerator and freezer safe. Our power came back on after 23 hours. There had been two small trees against the powerlines on our road which would have kept our power off, however I had taken the tractor and moved them off the lines. Having no visible problems,

Aftermath of Ice Storm: photo by Heather Warren

PSNH turned our road on after energizing the main feed. In our area most people went multiple days without power and it was two weeks or more before all the area was restored. During this time many people decided it was not important to get a Christmas tree. The few people who did come only bought a tree. Our wreath and soap sales completely stopped. The result was that we lost half of our net income for the year. Many of the people who did not get a tree told us they would never do that again, as Christmas day without a tree was not the same.

Chinese White Weeder Geese

Dad, being a Poultry Extension Specialist for the state of NH, knew a lot about poultry. He was well versed on Chinese weeder geese. In the late 70's he began using these geese to weed the strawberry patches after the picking season was over. These geese were light so they would not damage the strawberry plants when walking on them. If kept adequately hungry without being too hungry, they would do a nice job of eating most grass and small weeds. He used a short, 2 foot high electric fence to contain them in the field and a small secure pen to keep them safe from foxes at night. These geese became a trademark of the farm. Although these geese did not fly, when scared they could use their wings to clear the 2 foot fence. Once free of the field, usually the geese found their way to one of our two ponds. An open pond gate, a bit of grain or corn, and patience would entice the geese out of the pond to be caught and returned to the field. Dogs, humans, moose, and others were enough to scare these geese. Although the ponds were fenced, the mesh was big enough for these geese to squeeze through. In 1995, my wife and I took a rare few days off, leaving the high school age farm hands to tend the farm. Upon returning to the farm, these farm hands confessed that the geese had gotten out of their field and went to the pond. They told a tale of the many hours spent trying to catch these escapees. I opened the pond gate, threw a handful of corn on the ground outside the fence, stood back to allow the geese to exit the pond, closed the gate behind them and gently herded the geese back to their field, chasing them over their electric fence. This took about five ninutes. The farmhands thought I was a miracle worker. They old that story for years, and probably are still telling that story to heir children. One of our customers in the early 90's would enter he goose field and check the water buckets. She always found the buckets fairly full but dirty. She would then find me and, raising her voice, demand I give the geese clean water. I would tell her I would take care of it and she would either leave or go to picking berries but would give me a skeptical look. She would let me know she was appalled at my poor care of these creatures. One day she had enough of my poor care and began to yell at me with a number of other customers around. Well I had enough also. I sternly told her to come with me as I changed the water. I put fresh water in two buckets and demanded she watch for a few minutes. After we were a good distance from the buckets, the geese went to check them out. The geese put their beaks into the buckets one time only. Then they began putting their beaks into the ground and then back into the buckets. They were putting dirt into the water. She was astonished. Although angry, I explained to her that these were not people, they were geese. Geese process food through a gizzard which grinds food. Without grit they would die, thus they put dirt into their water. I then snidely said, "Don't put human values on animals!" She never checked the buckets again.

Barrington Natural Heritage and Agricultural Fairs

The Natural Heritage Committee is a subcommittee of the Barrington Conservation Committee. For many years the Natural Heritage Committee in Barrington held a Natural Heritage Day at various locations in Barrington. Properties with Conservation easements were the focus of these events. In 2009 and 2010 the Fahm hosted the Barrington Natural Heritage and Agricultural

Fairs. In 2009 a group of Barrington Farmers joined with the Natural Heritage Committee. In 2009, these groups set up a fair to be held in September to showcase local farmers, local land use issues, and responsible stewardship of natural resources. A lot of effort went in to the set up and logistics of the fair. There was talks about Natural Heritage, animals on display and for petting, mule wagon rides, local crafters, and a pig roast. It was a one day fair with no rain date. A farmers market was also set up at the Fahm for that day as we invited local farmers to attend and sell their bounty. Over 1000 people attended the fair. It was a huge success even though it rained. And it rained hard and long. By the end of the day we were very busy getting cars out of the muddy fields being used for parking. The focus of the day was on local agriculture and the farmers market was very successful. In 2010 the group decided to have a two day fair to protect against rain. More events and vendors were signed up and again the emphasis was to be on local agriculture. Local farmers were hoping for a repeat of the 2009 success. The fair came at the end of August and the weather was perfect except hot. The results were interesting. The people, who had come in 2009 to support local agriculture, came in 2010 to be entertained. The farmers market was a flop. The food vendors did alright but all others were disappointed. The hot weather probably aided this change as people do not cook as much in hot weather. The fair was well attended with approx. 1400 people between the two days. People had a great time, but the results were so disappointing that by the end of the 2nd day we knew we would not host it a third time. More lessons learned.

Auction 1997

After Dad died in early 1997, we decided to auction the excess contents of the Fahm to provide my siblings with some money.

The contents were my Mom's collections of Flow Blue, fine china, and depression glass as well as excess furniture, old tools and miscellaneous. One of our neighbor's had lost her husband and she had collected Flow Blue with my Mom. She was moving and had the Flow Blue china and other contents to sell. We combined the two lots for the auction. An auctioneer was hired, appraisals done, and Heather and I went through the list to keep the contents we wanted. A date was chosen for the auction and a large sign erected in our neighbor's field on Route 4. The day the sign was erected, Martha Stewart was in a neighboring town looking at properties to possibly buy. The rumors began that Martha Stewart had bought the Fahm. Other rumors that UNH had purchased the Fahm or that we had given the Fahm to UNH also started.

A large tent was set up in the front field and parking lots were set up. The auctioneer was to handle all the work for the auction including parking. A beautiful August day began with a flow of cars into the Fahm. The auctioneer's parking crew did not show up. I had a small Fahm crew and put them to work parking cars. We estimated over 1000 people were at the Fahm when the auction began. The parking situation got completely out of control and as the start time of the auction approached, people parked anywhere they thought they could. The roads to the parking lots became gridlocked. People were pulling into the Christmas tree fields and parking between Christmas trees and on top of small Christmas trees. This was the most angry I believe I have ever been before or after. I then directed my crew to park cars on one side of Warren Rd all the way to Route 4 while I straightened out the gridlock of cars in the rear roads. One of the crew came and told me they had no more room at the Route 4 end of Warren Rd just as I was getting the last of the gridlocked cars released. It had taken a full half hour to accomplish. The auction was a success but I am glad I never had to go through that again. When making arrangements for the Agricultural fair in '09 and '10 the lessons learned from this fiasco were included in our preparations and parking was never an issue. We arranged a large volunteer parking crew, a two mule wagon ride to transport people to and from the parking areas, and more than enough parking spaces. After the auction, we continued to have problems with the rumors that we were no longer operating the Fahm. It was four or five years before we stopped hearing the statement "I heard you were no longer here, I wish I had known".

Sheep and Balloons

Our local electric provider PSNH started a trial project in the late 90's. They would use sheep to graze the high tension line right of ways. This was an attempt to use less chemical controls. A flock would have about 250 sheep, a sheep dog that lived with the flock, two or 3 herding dogs and a shepherd. They were using the sheep south of our portion of the powerlines in 1999 when they decided to bring both flocks into our section at the same time. To get them to our section they had to go around the big swamp on our east border. The PSNH manager came to us and asked if we knew how they could get around the swamp. I did know and told them they would have to come in our woods roads to accomplish this. On a Saturday morning, 500 sheep with sheep dogs, herding dogs, and shepherds proceeded to travel through an abandoned town road, to our woods road, and on through the Fahm to the powerline. It went wonderfully. The only sounds were the hooves of the sheep on the gravel road and a whistle or voice command to the herding dogs. It also took very little time. Our youngest son Earl became good friends with the shepherds and spent a lot of time with them while on the powerline near the Fahm. Later in the summer when they had moved the flocks to another area, one of the shepherd's logs had given birth to pups and Earl was invited to see them. As the shepherd was cautioning Earl that the Mom might be protective, Earl climbed into the bathtub holding the Mom and pups and the Mom jumped into his lap. The shepherd was amazed and we were relieved.

On the Friday night before the sheep came through our roads, there was a hot air balloon festival in a neighboring town. About dusk, Earl and I were in the kitchen when we saw three boys coming in our road. Two were on bicycles and one on a motorbike. Since we did not allow motorbikes and I recognized these boys, we went out to ask them what they were doing, Before I could speak, one excitedly said " A balloon went down in the woods", and another said " And there is another one" as he pointed behind the farmhouse. We turned to see a hot air balloon trying to land in our back Christmas tree parking lot. The balloon was actually over a field of small Christmas trees and kept going down only to see the trees and go back up. Earl went with the boys to help that balloon find the parking lot, while I went up to the west field to see where the balloon had gone down in the woods. I arrived in the west field to find a balloon down in a road in our west Christmas tree field. It was not in the woods. Both balloon's crews were happy to be down. They had missed their landing areas and our fields were the first open fields without powerlines. They were both nervous whether I would be mad for landing at our Fahm. Apparently they have had landowners who weren't hospitable. I was thankful they had made an effort not to hurt any Christmas trees and we helped guide their chase crews to their locations. After they were packed up, each crew came to us with a bottle of champagne which is a tradition to give to the landowner. Since we don't drink champagne, I asked each if they had a picture of their balloon for Earl. One had a trading card of their balloon and the other after a lot of effort found a picture of his balloon. It was an exciting night. Between the balloon and sheep it was a weekend to remember!

1968 National 4-H Congress

From 1960 through 1968 I was a member of the 4-H organization. From 1960 to 1963 Barrington had an active 4-H club but this club disbanded and I was a Lone Member from 1964 through 1968. I believe my status was insured because of my father's position in the Cooperative Extension that also ran 4-H. In 1967 I entered a Poultry judging competition and won the NH state contest. A trip to Harrisburg, Pa for the regional competition was the prize. Our NH team came in third which did not qualify for the national competition. Our county Cooperative Extension Agent hoped that I could win a trip to the National 4-H Congress in 1968 but there were numerous 4-H members who raised poultry. After researching the various categories, the county agent suggested and mentored my entry for Field Crop Science for the state of NH. There was no competition so I easily won. Approximately 2000 4-H members attended the 1968 National 4-H Congress. It was held at the Conrad Hilton in Chicago, Illinois. The one big wrinkle to this event was that the National 4-H Congress was the first convention held in Chicago after the 1968 Democratic National Convention. The Conrad Hilton was where the Democratic candidate's headquarters were located. The rioting and police action during the 1968 Democratic Convention had been brutal. Wounded protesters had gone to the McCarthy or McGovern headquarters at the Conrad Hilton. That area of the hotel was closed off during the 4-H convention as the damage had not been repaired or cleaned up. Most of the 4-H delegates, myself included snuck to that floor to see for ourselves. I remember it being quite a mess. As for the 4-H Convention, here was 2000 young 15 to 19 year olds arriving in Chicago soon after the Democratic Convention and the press did not want to miss the action. Numerous television and radio news crews, both local and national were present at the start of the 4-H Convention hoping to catch the next big news events. This had never been the case in the past during the previous 4-H Congress's. But alas here were 2000 cleanly dressed, respectful, and reserved, mostly farm raised young people. It only took two to three days before all the tv and radio crews had left. There were no riots, no demonstrations and thus no news.

Off Road Trucks and Four Wheelers

One of the biggest changes in attitude over the years was the idea that a person could drive their vehicle wherever they wanted regardless of whose land it was. In the 50's and 60's, I do not recall a person driving on a woods road, powerline Right-of-Way, or the abandoned Two Mile road without permission. In the 80's as off road vehicles, snowmobiles, and four wheelers became popular, more people bought these type of vehicles without their own property to drive on. By 2000, we had at least 5 off road trucks driving onto our land and many trucks and four wheelers driving on the Two Mile road per year. Our powerline right of way went through a deep water swamp so those driving in, had to come out the same way. We would see them drive in and I would catch them driving out. I would ask them if they had permission to use the trail and usually they would say yes or tell me they did not need permission. Almost always they had temporary plates on the truck meaning they had recently purchased it. I usually would ask them if the land owner had given them permission, and if they said yes, I would scratch my head and tell them I did not recall giving them permission. Those who said they did not need permission would get a lesson on who owned the powerline right of way. One place on this trail went through a stone wall and it was a tight fit. A few truck owners got quite a surprise when they found out that the brush was hiding the stone wall. One trespasser was quite arrogant when I arrived to find his truck hung up on the wall. Two wheels were completely off the ground. As he told me not to bother him, I told him that I would not give permission for a tow truck to come retrieve his truck. He promptly changed his tune and decided he better become my friend. After I toyed with him a little more, I finally showed him how to jack his truck off the wall. The Two Mile road was a public way so we could not limit access. If a tree would fall down across the road, we would leave it and it usually would stay until somebody would cut it up and move it to the side. A couple times a truck would try to drive over a downed tree only to get hung up. When I heard the spinning tires and revving engines, I would go to the site of the stuck truck, give them my usual tirade about rutting the road (which was illegal), then I would help them remove the tree from under their truck. Every occasion where this happened, the truck had temporary plates. Throughout the years, I never saw the same person twice. We finally put large rocks and logs at trail openings to block access, but even these did not stop the occasional truck or four wheeler. We did not allow snowmobiles or four wheelers except a select few. These family members and friends helped watch over the land so that I was confident that I knew what was going on. The worst intrusion was in 2005 when a truck came into our west Christmas tree field which was planted with small seedlings about 2 feet tall. The resulting damage was about 150 trees demolished. Whoever it was had moved a boulder to get access to the field. After that I kept a keen eye on that field and twice had to intercept intruders. Both times it was four wheel drive jeeps with temporary plates. Once they drove in through our front yard. We had to completely limit snowmobiles, as other

Christmas tree farms had severe damage where snowmobiles could not see smaller trees under the snow. The snowmobiles would break the tops of the trees. We found that during the cut your own Christmas tree season we would have to fool proof our patches to keep people from driving into the patches. When it was wet, or if we had frost in the ground that had melted, it did not take much to stick a truck or car. The worst event was a man with his first four wheel drive truck who drove down a tractor road in a Christmas tree patch, got stuck in a low spot, and demolished numerous full size trees before I arrived at his location. He was trying to spin his way out. I had to cut an additional few trees to clear a path, and I pulled him out with the tractor. The funniest time was when a field was located about 200 feet from the parking lot and we had the area in front of the field fenced to keep cars out. I had to move a post to drive the tractor into the field. It was a busy day and it was frigid with howling winds. As I was working in the field I saw a car drive through the opening down to the patch and park. I was too busy to go address them so continued working. About 10 minutes later I looked and the edge of the patch looked like a new parking area with about 20 cars. This despite the numerous signs that said NO VEHICLES. I had to go back to the entrance and divert cars from entering until all those who had already entered were done and left. Then I could reinstall the post that prevented the cars from entering.

Christmas Tree Patch

Chapter 20: A Typical Day at the Fahm

Using the word typical is amusing. One of the benefits of farming is that no two days were the same. Until 1992 I was a person who needed multiple alarm clocks to wake up in the morning. Heather and I moved in with Dad at the Fahm in early 1992 and soon thereafter I began waking just before sunrise. This was a new experience for me and was very invigorating. As the sunrises changed so did my time of waking. A typical June morning would be to awake about 4:30 and let the dog and cat outside. I would have my first cigarette (I smoked until 2008) and my first cup of coffee. My day from there would depend on numerous questions. Were we going to be open that day? Did we have harvesting to do? Had the raspberries been pruned such that they were ready for July harvest? What was the weather? Was there equipment to fix? Was there planting to do? Did I need to scout for animal damage? Was irrigating necessary? Did I have to scout the strawberry patch for picking conditions? Many more questions went through my head. About 5am or 5:30 I would go out to do whatever I had decided was my first priority. A great benefit of working on the Fahm was that about every two hours I could go into the house, have a coffee, visit with Earl and Heather if they were home, and take a break that would refresh me. After the break I could go to work for another couple hours. I actually had the freedom to take these breaks whenever I wanted. If it was possible I took a nap at noon. I relished this nap and always looked forward to it all morning. I then would wake up two hours later feeling refreshed and go back to work. I was much more productive after a nap. I consider myself as a professional napper.

There were many tasks that were dictated by the calendar. The outside gardening year began about April 1 with uncovering the strawberry plants that had been covered with mulch hay in late November. Next would be ground preparation which included plowing, tilling, and at times plastic mulch laying. This was tractor work primarily and was the least boring. April 20 was a target date to begin planting new strawberry beds for future years. May 1st was a target date to begin the large task of pruning the raspberries. This was to remove the dead canes from the previous year and thin the new green canes for optimum yield. The majority of this work was done on my knees. Usually I could do what I called stints which meant I could work at this task for a few hours but then would switch to a different task for the rest of that day. Since pruning raspberries took approximately 120 hours, I usually was still doing stints of this task well into June. Other work in May involved planting the vegetable crops, irrigating, land tillage, weeding, a small amount of harvesting, mowing, planting Christmas trees, and scouting fields often for any issues. Planting continued through July of various small crops. The last planting of the year was garlic in late October. By August, irrigating, harvesting and tending customers at the farm stand were the main tasks. In September shaping Christmas trees and mowing the Christmas tree patches would be added to the task list. With the fall weather and lack of bugs, this was the nicest working weather of the year. November brought wreath making and set up for the Christmas tree season. The weekend before Thanksgiving we opened daily for the Christmas tree season. We were open every day until Christmas except Thanksgiving Day. January brought paperwork, equipment repair, brush cutting, building repair, equipment and seed purchasing, and a more relaxing schedule.

Whenever the farm store was open, it needed to be tended. Heather spent the most time managing and tending the store. Our niece's Amy and Kirstin each spent a few summers at the store. Our children also spent time at the store with Earl spending the most time. I spent time whenever necessary and the last two years did a lot of double duty where I would tend customers but work on other chores between customers.

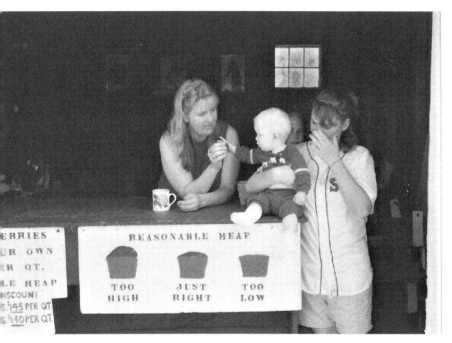

Heather Tending Farm Stand with Earl, Jen, and Richard Behind.

Chapter 21: The Final Chapter, Selling the Fahm

I never imagined that it would be me who would sell the Fahm. In 2007, I came to the realization that I was no longer enjoying the Fahm as I once had. The financial realities and hardships had taken a toll on me and money was becoming the main focus. Also I was greatly bothered that I was no longer keeping up with the building maintenance due to cost and time. I blurted out to Heather that I was done farming, and her reaction insured that I would not mention this again anytime soon. This did begin a conversation that led to a lot of discussion about our age and that we wanted to stay in control and not get to the point that we had to sell. After discussing our situation with numerous farming financial people, in early 2011 we decided to pursue selling. Our accountant had suggested we get five appraisals and since we already had a current appraisal from our Farm Credit bank, we proceeded to get four more. These varied so much that we knew how unique our property was. No one was sure what the value was, but we knew that it was what one person would pay. The real estate agent we chose was named Lisa. She was wonderful and understood this property. She told us it would probably take two years to sell, but I did not believe it would take that long. In our area, two other farms had gone on the market so now there were three unique properties available. In July 2011, we announced that the Fahm was for sale. We notified the local newspaper and they did a front page article on the Fahm. People flocked to the Fahm. Over the next few months we had a low ball offer from a neighbor. He wanted the land as he abutted it. We had people who upon finding out what the conservation easement meant, decided it did not fit their plans. We had people who thought the house was a tear-down, others who thought it needed updating and a few who loved the character as is. And we had a number of people who would love to buy the Fahm but were not sure what the value was. We had one family offer our asking price but on condition we accept half down, stay at the Fahm, and the other half in four years. I graciously thanked them but let them know that we might be there another four years but I was not going to enlist. One of the other farms available sold to a developer as it was not protected by a conservation easement. This farm now has grown lots of houses. The other farm kept dropping its price but they removed the house from the sale, leaving the land and the farm store for sale. It did have a conservation easement. It sold to a man who revived the farm store business and now it is thriving again. We had a family who loved the Fahm but hoped for a less expensive farm. On their second visit, I told them that my agent, Lisa had said that whoever buys the Fahm will drive in and know that they are going to live here. The young lady looked at me and said, "That person is already here". We negotiated off and on for months. She was right as we sold the Fahm to her and her boyfriend, now husband. Our agent Lisa was right as it took two years. They have added livestock to the Fahm in a big way. They have opened more land for grazing and are doing much needed maintenance on the buildings. They began a CSA which stands for Community Supported Agriculture. They have changed the name of the Fahm to Brasen Hill Farm and now are the stewards of this wonderful property. Once we sold, we heard numerous people lament that they did not act sooner, but I truly believe that the new stewards are the right ones!

After we had agreed to the sale, next came a great effort to clean out 67 years of accumulation from the buildings. Hired help, trash trucks (3 loads), lots of boxes, a storage unit, a continuing yard sale at the farm stand, family going through contents and pictures, craigslist ads, a two day moving party, and a lot of forgotten memories recovered ensued. Some treasures but mostly trash were found. We were able to clean out everything except the barn. That building had so much accumulation that we ran out of time. We should have started cleaning out the Fahm earlier, many years earlier! The cellar, house attics, carriage house and shell house were cleaned out to a point I had never seen before. It was a great relief when we ended our effort and drove off the Fahm for the last time as owners. This beautiful land and buildings began its next chapter.

I now tell people that," I use to be a tired farmer, now I am a retired farmer. Retired is better than tired."

Throughout my stewardship of the Fahm, numerous people asked what they could do to support local agriculture. I learned that they need to vote for their local farms. How do you vote for a local farm? You vote with your wallet!

Our Children: Earl, Russell, Richard and Jennifer

References:

Warren, Peter Whitson, <u>The Farm</u> (A History and Photographic Documentaion of The Peletiah Daniels Farm Barrington NH) 1985

Made in the USA
Columbia, SC
13 June 2017